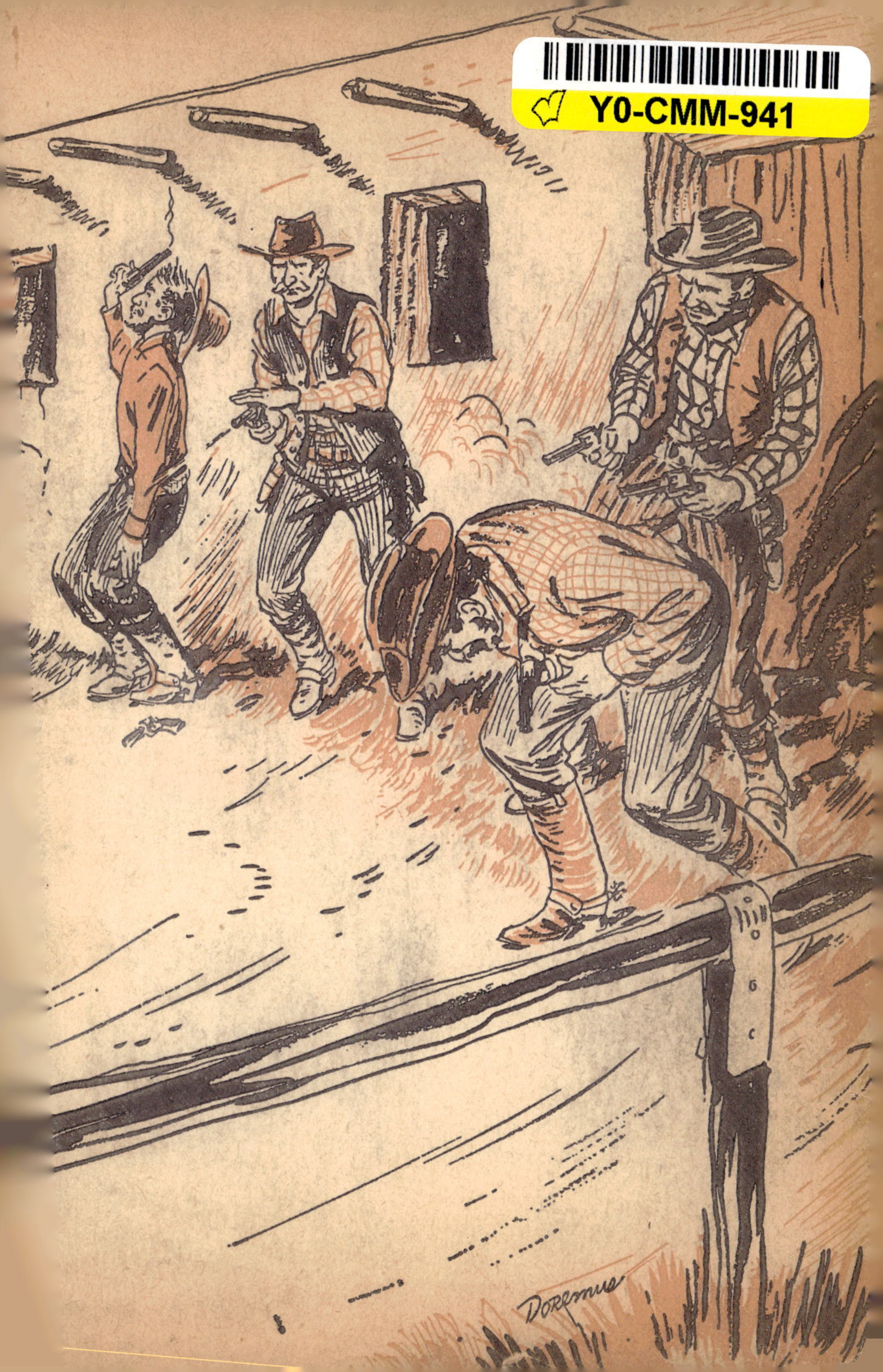
Doremus

Wyatt Earp

By
PHILIP KETCHUM

Illustrated by
ROBERT DOREMUS

WHITMAN PUBLISHING COMPANY
RACINE, WISCONSIN

Copyright © 1956 by

WHITMAN PUBLISHING COMPANY

Printed in U.S.A.

The publishers and the author acknowledge their indebtedness to "WYATT EARP, Frontier Marshal," by Stuart N. Lake, the definitive work about WYATT EARP, published by Houghton Mifflin Company of Boston and New York, copyright 1931 by Stuart N. Lake, and express their thanks to the publishers and the author of said work for their permission to base certain portions of this book upon it.

CONTENTS

1. Death on the Prairie 9
2. The Town That Lived in Fear 25
3. Marshal for an Hour 40
4. The Wrong Side of the Law 57
5. Trapped 76
6. The Marshal of Wichita 86
7. The Gathering Storm 104
8. The Desperate Hours 118
9. The Showdown 132
10. The Finishing Touches 146
11. A New Job 160
12. Wyatt Meets a Killer 175
13. A Price on His Head 191
14. A Town Is Tamed 205
15. The Road to Tombstone 222
16. Lead Poison 236
17. The Feud 248
18. The Final Decision 267

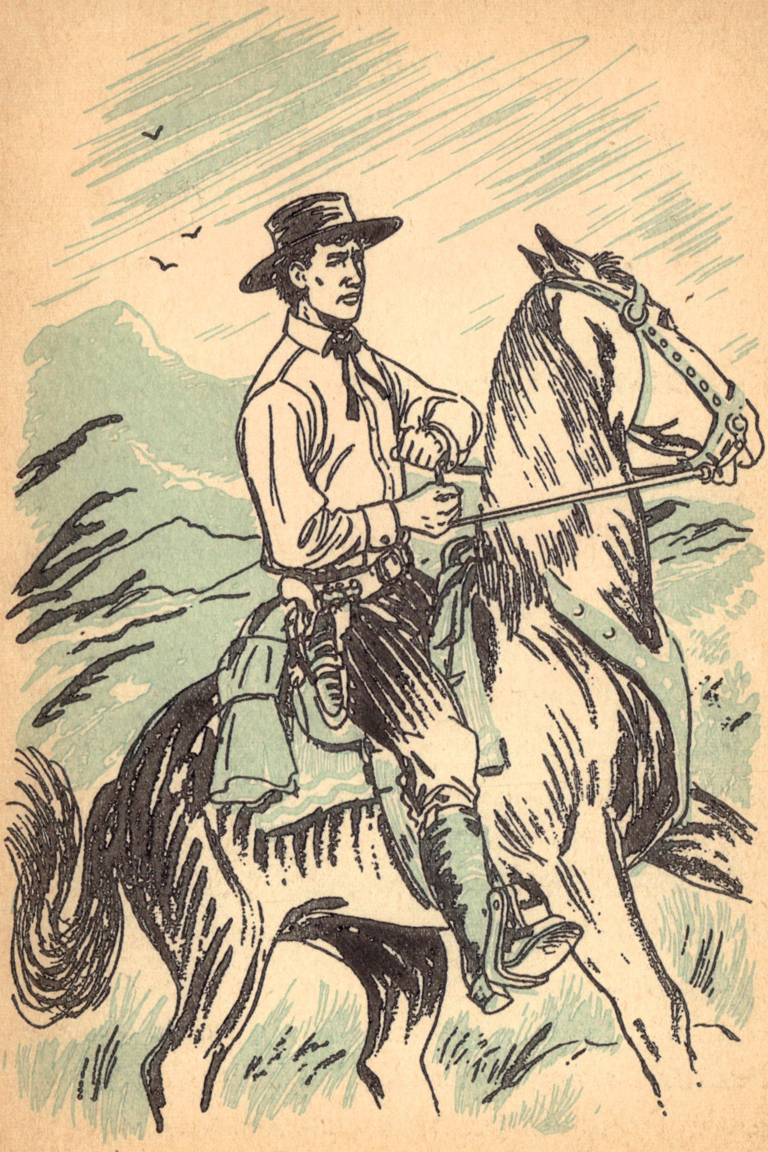

1. DEATH ON THE PRAIRIE

In 1873 the wagon road through central Kansas from Abilene to Ellsworth followed the twisting course of Smoky Hill River. It was a well-marked road, its ruts cut deep by the iron-rimmed wheels of thousands of supply wagons which had traveled westward to the wild, booming towns along the frontier. Near it was a trail worn smooth by horsemen, and along this trail one afternoon in August, rode a young man, who in Ellsworth, had a date with destiny.

Wyatt Earp, that year, was twenty-five. He was tall, slender, well muscled. He had brown hair, clear blue eyes, a straight nose, and a square-cut jaw, which to some might have betrayed the stubbornness of his nature. He was dressed in the rough, serviceable clothing which most men wore in this part of the country, and like most others, he carried two guns belted around his waist. They were single action, Colt .45's, the frontier model, popularly known as "The Peacemaker."

Nothing in Wyatt's appearance gave any indication as to what his background had been like. Few men, to look at him, would have guessed that he had crossed the country to California in a covered wagon caravan when he was only sixteen; or that at seventeen he had driven a stage run between San Bernardino and the pueblo of Los Angeles, making a round trip each day.

It also might have been hard to believe that for a time he had owned and operated his own freighting outfit, or that he had put in several seasons as a buffalo hunter, and had acquired a considerable reputation as a marksman, and as a man able to handle his guns.

Yet all this, and more, was true. He had fought the Sioux Indians in crossing the plains, had had his first brush with outlaws when driving a stage. And in his pocket this afternoon he carried several thousand dollars, the profits of his sale of the buffalo hides he had taken. In those days, few young men of twenty-five could boast of having earned that much money, honestly.

Wyatt held his horse at a steady lope along the trail. It

was a cloudy day, but the heat of the sun came through the clouds, making it hot and sticky. Perspiration plastered his shirt to his body. He had covered well over two-thirds of the distance to Ellsworth. Late tonight, if he kept riding, he might reach the town, but he wasn't sure that such a plan was wise.

Ellsworth boasted of a regular population of three hundred, but right now, toward the end of the cattle-driving season, hundreds of cowboys who had come up the trail from Texas, would be camped in and around the town. For this reason, he doubted that he could find a room anyplace, and if he had to camp out, it might be smart to camp out along the trail rather than near the town. Along the trail there was less chance of being bothered by someone who might be interested in robbing him of the money he carried.

From somewhere up ahead he heard the sudden sound of shooting. He reined up, every muscle in his body tightening. He counted the shots. There were five, close together, then two more, then another. And after that, complete and ominous silence.

The sound of the shooting had the same effect on Wyatt as it always had had in the past, and always would have in the future. It sobered him instantly, driving all other thoughts from his mind. It sharpened his senses and sent through his body a warning signal to be on guard for whatever might happen.

He knew that the shooting might have been nothing more than target practice but he also was aware of the fact that it might be an indication of trouble. These were lawless days. Most of the men in this frontier country were men like himself, who worked for what they made; but among them were those who didn't work. Renegades and outlaws they were, who lived by the terror of their guns, and to whom life was cheap.

He loosened his Colts so they could be drawn swiftly if he needed them, then rode on forward. Suddenly he pulled up. A hundred yards ahead, the trail he was following twisted away from the river to turn through a fold in the hills on a cutoff. And coming down that cutoff, breaking into view, were four mounted men, racing their horses at top speed.

Wyatt had no chance, now, to avoid meeting them. He could have turned away and ridden for the trees along the river, but it never had been his way to run from anything. It never would be. And so he sat waiting, one hand tight on the reins of his horse, the other swinging close to one of his holstered guns.

The four men pounded on toward him without slackening the speed of their horses. One turned to shout something to the others. What it was, he couldn't hear. But he could guess. *There had been trouble up there on the trail, otherwise these men wouldn't be riding so hard. He was close enough to be a witness to their escape, which meant he was in a dangerous spot. Men who dealt in crime didn't like to leave witnesses to what they had done.*

As they drew nearer, Wyatt marked how they looked. Two were big, almost fat, and had bushy, black beards. The other two were of average size, thinner, and one of these seemed rather old and rode hunched over his saddle.

It was one of the bearded men who had shouted to the others as they came through the fold in the hills and saw him, and that same man now gave another order, shouting it as they came close, and whipping out his holster gun.

"All right. Let him have it."

Wyatt had been in tight spots before, and would be again. But never one which developed so suddenly, or so brutally. The four men riding down on him split up, so that two would pass him on either side and thus catch him in a cross fire. All four now had drawn their guns. They meant to shoot him down in cold blood. They meant to take no chances that he would escape.

As the gun of the bearded leader centered on him, his right arm snapped up, lifting his Colt smoothly from its holster. He had thumbed the hammer back before the gun was leveled, and the sound of his shot merged with the explosion of the shot fired by the bearded man. A bullet whistled harmlessly past his head, but the bearded man threw up his hands, then sagged forward in his saddle.

Wyatt fired at one of the other men. Then, as his horse started plunging, he pitched himself from the saddle, landing on his side. He fired a shot at the third man, rolled over in the rough buffalo grass and came to his knees, ready to fire again.

But a fourth shot wasn't needed. The fourth man was racing away, crouching low over the saddle of his horse. He was firing back, but his shots were wild. The others trailed after him, two reeling helplessly in the saddle, badly hit.

Wyatt got to his feet. The man who had been firing back at him had emptied his gun, and now, at a safe distance, had pulled up and probably was reloading it.

The other three were grouping there with him.

"Come on back," Wyatt said aloud. "If you haven't had enough, come on back."

But he didn't mean it. He hoped they wouldn't come back. His stomach was starting to churn. It always did at a time like this. He didn't like shooting at another human being. He never would feel right about it. In the days ahead as in the past, he would use his gun against other men, but only in self-defense or when absolutely necessary. And always he would aim his shots as he had today, to cripple an enemy rather than to take his life.

He reloaded and holstered his gun, and after that, mopped his hand across his perspiring face while still watching the four men. They had dismounted. Two were lying down while the other two bent over them, probably to care for their wounds.

"All right," Wyatt said. "Stay there for a while. I'll ride on ahead and see what happened up the trail. I'll see what it is you didn't want me to know about . . . and maybe I'll be back."

He caught and mounted his horse and turned through the fold in the hills in the direction from which the four men had come.

A quarter of a mile up the short cut, two horses were standing at the side of the trail, and not far away, two figures lay on the ground. Wyatt hurried forward, and as he drew near, one of the figures moved, struggled to sit up. He saw, with a sense of shock, that it was a boy of sixteen or seventeen, a boy with a shock of sandy hair, matted with blood from a scalp wound.

Wyatt dismounted, stepped to his side. Eyes as blue as his own stared up at him.

"You're—not one of them," the boy said in a husky whisper.

"Nope, I'm not one of them," Wyatt answered.

He turned to examine the other figure lying on the ground. It was the figure of an older man with a sweeping mustache and a deeply lined face. He had been shot several times in the chest. It took Wyatt only a moment to realize there was nothing to be done for him. He turned away, pulling off his hat.

"He's not—dead, is he?" the boy asked.

"I'm afraid he is," Wyatt said bleakly.

The boy got to his knees. He crawled closer to the silent figure of the older man. He reached out to touch his father's shoulder.

"Dad," he whispered. "Dad!"

Tears were swimming in his eyes. He tried desperately to blink them away, but couldn't. The boy was quite thin, but looked tall for his age. A holster was belted around his waist but it was empty.

"I'd better take care of that wound in your scalp," Wyatt said. "It still is bleeding."

"That doesn't matter," the boy said in a weary voice. "Nothing matters now."

"If everyone felt that way, the world would have ended long ago," Wyatt said. "I have a notion your father was proud of you, but he wouldn't be proud of what you just said. He wouldn't be proud of a quitter."

"It's easy for you to say that," the boy answered. "He wasn't your father."

"I imagine he was a fine man," Wyatt said.

"The finest."

"And if he was alive, what would he say to you now?"

The boy took a deep breath. He squared his shoulders and scowled at Wyatt.

"Who are you?" he demanded.

"Folks call me Wyatt Earp. What's your name?"

"Jeff Crandall."

"And your father was—"

"Sam Crandall. We're from the Red River country, in Texas."

"You came up the trail with a herd of longhorns?"

Jeff nodded. "We sold them in Ellsworth. We paid off the men, and started out this morning for Abilene."

"And what happened, Jeff?"

"Nothing till we got here, where we met four men. They were coming along the trail toward us. When they got close they covered us with their guns. We didn't even have a warning they were going to draw them."

"And then what?"

"They demanded the money belt Dad was carrying. They seemed to know all about it, but they were coming from the direction of Abilene."

"They could have circled around in front of you," Wyatt said. "That's probably what they did. They let you ride quite a distance from Ellsworth. They picked this place for the holdup. It's a good spot. Not much chance of anyone seeing them, and no chance for you or your father to see them before it was too late to avoid them. Go on with your story. Did your father hand over the money belt when they asked for it?"

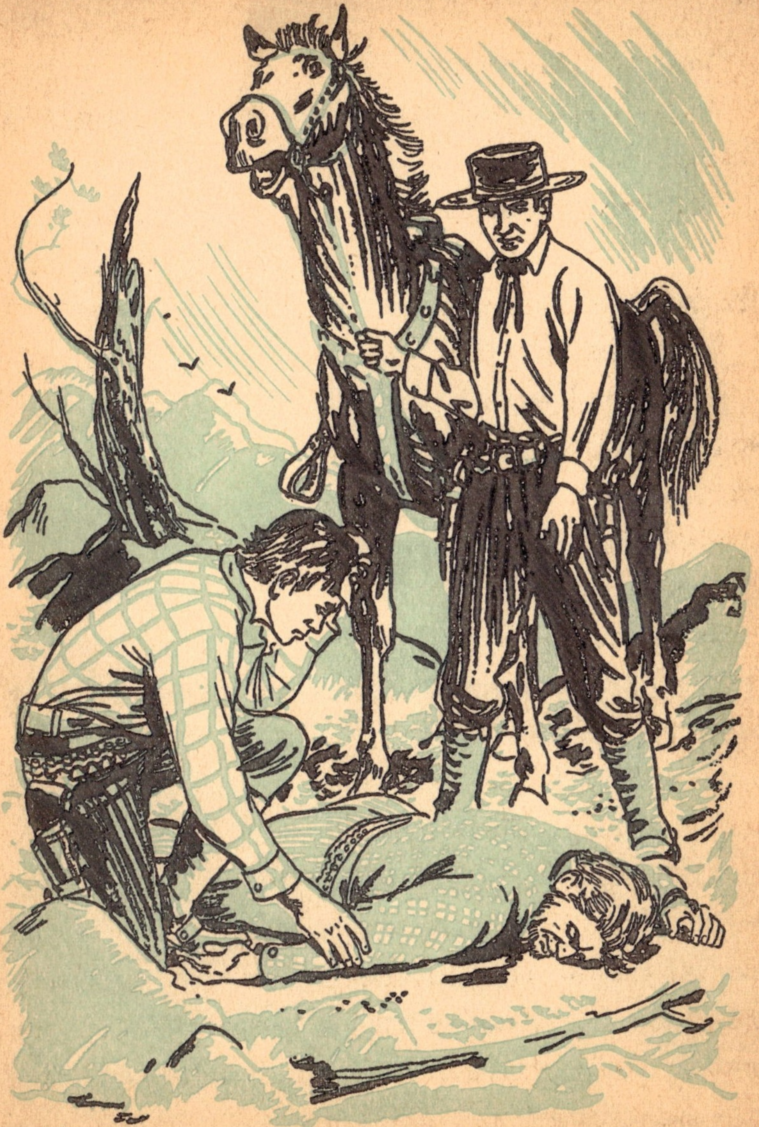

Jeff nodded. "Dad turned to me and said, 'Fifteen thousand dollars isn't worth dying for.' Then he handed over the money belt."

"And what started the shooting?"

"Nothing," Jeff answered. "That is, the minute the men got the money belt, they just started shooting. I—something hit me in the head. That's all I remember."

Wyatt wasn't greatly surprised at the boy's story. Here was an instance of brutal murder, but it was typical of what was happening all over the state of Kansas. The holdup men had been given the money they were after and could have ridden off with it without further molesting the Crandalls. But they had stayed to kill them, possibly afraid Sam Crandall might hunt them down if they didn't put an end to his life. They undoubtedly thought they had killed the boy, too. The bloody scalp wound Jeff had received easily could have deceived them.

"They got away, didn't they?" Jeff said.

"But not without being hurt a little," Wyatt replied, remembering his fight with the men. "And maybe they haven't gone so far that we can't catch up with them. After you let me fix that head of yours, we'll take a look-see."

He had salve and a bandage in his saddlebags, and after

he had dressed Jeff's wound, he climbed back on his horse again.

"You wait here," he ordered. "I may be back in a few minutes, or it may be an hour or more."

"I'd like to go with you," Jeff said.

"And leave your father here alone?" Wyatt answered. "No, you stay with him."

He turned back in the direction from which he had come, but when out in the open again, he saw no sign of the four men.

He reined up, then, and sat his horse for a time, considering what he should do. Two of the four men were badly wounded. That meant they couldn't travel too fast and that he might easily overtake them. But the night wasn't far off and if he didn't run them down before dusk, it might take another day to come up with them. He couldn't guess which way they would turn after it grew dark.

He had another matter to worry about, too. Up the cut-off was a sixteen-year-old boy who was considerably broken up over the death of his father. Tonight, and probably tomorrow, Jeff Crandall needed someone he could talk to, someone to bolster up his courage. And a thing like that probably was more important than getting back the fifteen thousand dollars which had been stolen. Jeff could earn more money in the days ahead. And as for the outlaws, the life of an outlaw seldom was long. Sooner or later, justice had a way of catching up with those who failed to live by the law.

He rode back up the trail to where Jeff was waiting.

"They're gone," he reported. "I could chase after them, but it might take days to ride them down."

"You're only one man, anyhow," Jeff said. "They're four."

Wyatt smiled. He asked, "Jeff, what are your plans?"

"I don't know," Jeff answered. "I guess I haven't any."

"Do you have relatives anywhere?"

"No."

"Then you're all alone in the world. But you're nearly man-size. I'll bet you can rope and ride well, and handle cattle."

"Yes. That I can do."

"Then you need a job, don't you?"

"I hadn't thought about it, but I guess I do."

"Think about it," Wyatt said. "I know a few people in Ellsworth who might be able to put you to work. How would you like to ride there with me?"

"I might as well ride there as anyplace," Jeff said. And then he looked at his father's body, and shuddered, and added, in a low voice, "We have something to do here, first."

He had come up the trail from Texas. He had seen men die before. He knew perfectly well the job that lay ahead of them. There would be no point in taking his father's body back to Ellsworth. Here on the trail where he had died was as appropriate a place for his father's grave as any other.

"I'll do the digging," Wyatt said.

He set to work scraping out a shallow grave, then gathered rocks with which to cover it. He decided that he and Jeff would camp here tonight, then ride on in the morning.

He paid little attention to the boy. He knew Jeff was crying, but he was afraid he would feel like crying himself if anything like this happened to his father, or to one of his brothers. He felt angry. Angry that such a thing as this could happen. This was a great country but he was beginning to believe it never would be a fine country until something was done to tame the unruly men who had come here, and who held human life to be of little value.

"A day's coming when someone's going to have to do something about it," he said under his breath.

He didn't know, then, that he was going to have more to do than anyone else with the taming of the West.

2 • THE TOWN THAT LIVED IN FEAR

They rode on in the morning as soon as it was light. Jeff looked pale and tired. He probably hadn't slept much. And he was silent during the early part of the morning. Nothing Wyatt could say encouraged him to talk.

Now, as they followed the trail along the river and drew near the town of Ellsworth, they could see cattle everywhere they looked, and here and there, the camps of the riders herding them, and keeping the different herds bunched and separate from each other.

"They told me in Abilene," Wyatt mentioned, "that there were close to 150,000 head of Texas cattle grazing the prairies around Ellsworth, and awaiting shipment east."

"Maybe so," Jeff said.

"Of course, all the cattle we're seeing won't be shipped east," Wyatt continued. "Some will be held on the range to fatten, and to wait for a better market price. That's what interests me. I've a notion there's money to be made in buying up Texas cattle, and in fattening them, and holding them for a better market price."

This was something that had been on Wyatt Earp's mind all summer. He had traveled over a good part of Kansas looking for some proposition along that line which might interest him. It was what had taken him to Abilene, and now was taking him to Ellsworth.

"Dad and I had been planning on going back to Texas," Jeff said. "Maybe we would have bought cattle there, and driven them up the trail next year. Now I don't know what I'll do."

His mind was still on his father and on the tragedy which had overtaken them. Wyatt knew that was perfectly natural.

"You might throw in with me if I buy up cattle here," he suggested.

Jeff glanced at him, for the first time showing an interest in what he was saying.

"Would you like that?" Wyatt asked.

"Yes, I think I would. But would cattle fatten on this kind of grass?"

"It's the best graze you can find," Wyatt answered.

"Folks around here call it grama grass. I call it buffalo grass. It's what the great herds of buffaloes fed on. There were hundreds of thousands of buffaloes here before men started killing them off for their hides. This year, alone, close to 'half a million hides will be shipped east from Dodge."

"I've never seen a buffalo," Jeff said.

"Maybe next year you can hunt them—if we don't go into the cattle business."

"That—that I really would like," Jeff said, his eyes sparkling.

They continued talking of buffalo hunting, but even as they discussed it, Wyatt wondered if it would be profitable next year. It might not be. The buffalo herds had been thinned out to a terrible extent during recent years.

"Well, we may try it," Wyatt said. "I've an idea you would make a good buffalo hunter, Jeff."

"We're getting close to Ellsworth," Jeff said finally, changing the subject.

"That's right," Wyatt nodded.

Jeff looked at him, scowling, and after a moment said, "Mr. Earp, one of these days I'm going to find those four men who shot my father, and when I do—"

"And when you do, what then, Jeff?" Wyatt asked quietly.

"I'll kill them."

Wyatt frowned. "Did you ever kill a man?"

"No."

"It doesn't leave you feeling very good, Jeff. It gives you a knot in the stomach. It makes you kind of sick. It's a serious thing to take another man's life."

"Not a murderer's life."

"Yes, even a murderer, for who are you to judge what drove him to murder? No law, Jeff, gives one man the right of life or death over another. Even a confessed murderer is entitled to a trial, to a day in court."

The boy's scowl had deepened. "Just the same, if I meet them—"

"If you meet them," Wyatt interrupted, "get in touch with the nearest marshal, or officer of the law."

"The nearest officer of the law," Jeff scoffed. "Wait until you see what law officers they've got in Ellsworth. They stay under cover all day. Ben Thompson runs the town the way he wants to—he and his men."

"So Ben Thompson's in Ellsworth, is he?" Wyatt said.

"You bet he is. And tell me this. Where would you find

an officer brave enough to go up against Ben Thompson?"

Wyatt could offer no answer to the question Jeff had asked. He had met Ben Thompson and he knew something of his history. Certainly, in all his life along the frontier, Thompson hadn't run into a lawman courageous enough to oppose him.

Thompson was a Texan who had fought in the Confederate army during the war, and who afterwards had gone to Mexico for a time. For the past half dozen years, he and his brother, and the tough, hard crowd they led, had drifted from one booming frontier town to another, and had made their own law in each place where they stopped. Usually the marshal or sheriff of a town the Thompsons were visiting found it to his advantage to be out of town on business, while the Thompsons were there. That way, he might live longer.

How many men the Thompsons had killed, Wyatt didn't know, but the list was quite long.

"You're sure the Thompsons are in town?" he asked after a time.

"Dad knew them down in Texas," Jeff answered. "He pointed them out to me day before yesterday and told me about them. He said there was a marshal and three deputies in Ellsworth, as well as a county sheriff, but that none of them had the nerve to try to stop Ben Thompson from doing whatever he wanted to do."

"No man can be a law to himself," Wyatt muttered. "Nor can any group of men take over the law and use it to serve their own ends."

"But that's what's happening in Ellsworth."

Wyatt shrugged. "So it's happening in Ellsworth. But it's a condition that'll be changed, Jeff. I don't know how or when it'll be changed, but the change is bound to come. That's one thing I'm sure of."

"Why, Mr. Earp?"

"Because it isn't right that one man, or group of men, should terrorize others."

"Who will stop it?"

"Men who believe as I do. Men who believe in law, and justice, and in the triumph of right over wrong."

"Someone has to start it, before there will be a change," Jeff said practically.

"Yes," Wyatt agreed. "Someone has to start it."

Ellsworth had grown up on the bank of Smoky Hill River. It had been a quiet, sleepy town until the railroad came, and with the railroad, a number of enterprising men who saw the possibility of building Ellsworth into the cattle center of the world.

There was good reason for their optimism and the grand plans they made. To the north, west, south, and east of the town were thousands of acres of the finest grazing lands anywhere. Here was room for the pasturing and fattening of the great herds of longhorns being driven up from Texas each year. Here in Ellsworth might be the foundations of a great city.

In the summer of 1873 the dream seemed very possible. Herd after herd coming up the trail had made Ellsworth its destination, and in Ellsworth, that summer, there were more cattle buyers than ever before had assembled at one place. Along the railroad tracks which ran near the river, cattle pens had been built.

In the town, of course, there wasn't room for all the new people moving in, but around it, sod houses, shacks, and tents were thrown up, and for a man who couldn't find a bed, there were always the stars he could sleep under. In Kansas, in the summer, it seldom cooled off at night. Sleeping out was a pleasure.

The town was a barren and ugly place. No trees grew

in its plaza, and the streets were ankle-deep with dust. Most of the business houses were frame structures, hastily built, some with porches and false fronts but many more without.

By day and by night the hitching rails around the plaza and along the street were crowded with cow ponies. And by day and by night, the streets and the plaza were thronged with men. Cow hands working the range around Ellsworth, drovers just up the trail from Texas, buffalo hunters, teamsters, land sellers and buyers, cattle sellers and buyers. Men with a job and those without, some looking for a good time, others for a chance to earn the money to buy a meal. Men of many nationalities, colors, and creeds. Some armed, some not. A good share of those who didn't seem to be armed carried a hidden gun.

Wyatt Earp had seen many a town like Ellsworth. He could pick out the cow hands just up the trail from Texas, men who were noisy and loud and were celebrating the end of the long drive. Such men usually didn't have trouble on their minds and wouldn't deliberately provoke a fight, but might easily be drawn into one.

He could spot the cattle buyers by the way they dressed, and could single out, by their attitudes, those whom he would have watched closely if he had happened to be marshal.

During his first day in town he learned how completely Ben Thompson dominated the affairs of Ellsworth. Ben Thompson, his brother Bill, and those who traveled with them had set up headquarters in a place called the Grand Central. There, they separated men from their money. They did this through crooked gambling games, or through the simpler process of knocking a man over the head, and robbing him. The man might afterwards complain to the sheriff or one of his deputies, but nothing ever came of such a complaint.

Almost hourly there were fights in the Grand Central, or behind it, or in front of it. Fist fights, knife fights, gun fights. Wyatt saw several men seriously injured. He saw three killed. And he noticed with a growing contempt how the law officers took cover whenever Ben Thompson's men were on the prowl.

But while all this interested him, Wyatt didn't lose sight of the mission which had brought him to Ellsworth. He talked to every cattle buyer he could find, asking questions about the market and the possibility that the price offered for cattle might be better next year.

The answers he got were discouraging. Most men to whom he talked thought the prices offered next year would be even lower. They seemed so certain of this, Wyatt wondered if it wouldn't be better to spend the next season hunting buffalo, and to put off his venture into the cattle business until times improved.

He was turning this problem over in his mind on the afternoon of August eighteenth as he lounged on the porch of Beebe's General Store, which fronted on the plaza. A scorching sun blazed down from the sky. The day was uncomfortably hot. There was no stirring breeze in the air. The dust kicked up by the men crossing and recrossing the street made it hard to breathe.

From one of the establishments down the street there came a sudden clamor of noise, of angry, shouting voices.

"Just another fight," Wyatt thought. Another of the many fights which were such common occurrences in Ellsworth.

The door of the place burst open, and two men came out. Ben and Bill Thompson! They went running toward the Grand Central, shouting back angrily at those who had followed them into the street.

Wyatt straightened. Any time Ben and Bill Thompson

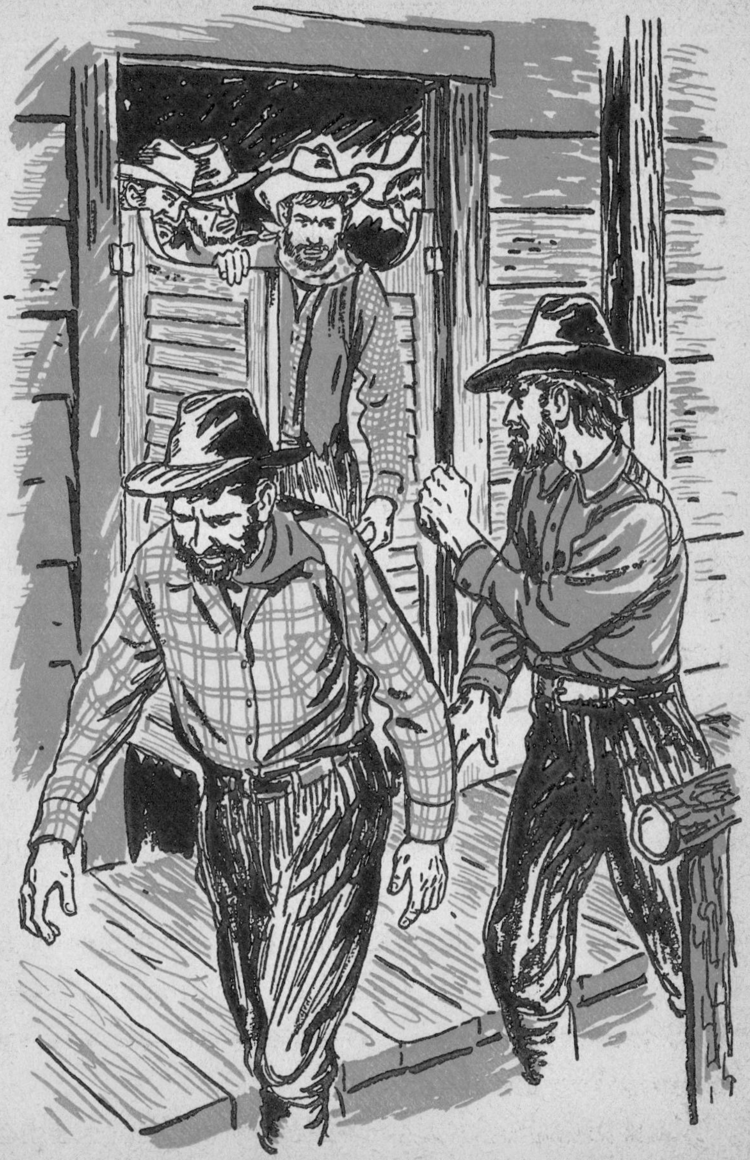

started running, it was a fact to be noted. And any time Ben and Bill Thompson got stirred up, something was sure to happen. They looked stirred up this afternoon. And they meant to cause trouble for someone.

That was apparent when they came out of the Grand Central, Ben carrying a double-barreled shotgun, and Bill, a rifle. A hayrack was tied in front of the building from which they had fled in anger, and now they took up positions behind it, and shouted to the men inside to come out and fight.

Men were pouring into the street from every building. Wyatt heard someone say that Bill Thompson had had a fist fight, had been knocked down, and had gone after his gun to get even with the man who had struck him. Ben Thompson, of course, was backing up his brother, for the man who had fought with Bill had friends.

Sheriff Whitney came down the street, and this afternoon Whitney showed a rare brand of courage. He wasn't armed, but in spite of this he walked up to the Thompsons and ordered them off the street.

"Keep out of this, Whitney," Ben roared. "We're goin' to get those men in there."

Whitney went in to talk to those for whom the Thompsons were waiting. He returned to report that the man who had knocked Bill down had escaped by the back door, and had invited the Thompsons into a place known as Brennan's, to talk things over. After a few minutes Whitney continued up the dusty street and, when he saw Wyatt Earp standing on the porch of the store, stopped to speak to him.

"They've calmed down a lot," he commented. "Of course, their own crowd has gathered around them and could stir them up again. But maybe not."

"Did you take their guns away from them?" Wyatt inquired.

"Nope—they never would have stood for it," Whitney answered.

It was Wyatt's personal opinion, based on what he had seen in towns like this, that serious trouble never could be avoided until men were forced to check their guns someplace, as soon as they rode in. Guns bred trouble—a man's temper became shorter with a Colt to back it up.

He was about to suggest this to Whitney when the door to Brennan's was thrust open and Bill Thompson stepped out into the street. He was carrying Ben's shotgun. His face was flushed, perspiring.

"Maybe I won't get the man who knocked me down," he shouted, "but at least, I'll get a sheriff."

He raised the gun to his shoulder, and as Whitney jerked around to face him, he fired both barrels.

Whitney grabbed at his breast. He lurched backward and would have fallen if Wyatt hadn't caught him. He whispered something, something about wanting to be taken home. But Wyatt, staring down at him, doubted if he would live long enough to make it.

He bent over the dying man. He looked up from the sheriff into the blazing eyes of the man who had pulled the trigger and he saw that Ben Thompson had come out of Brennan's to line up with his brother. He saw others coming out, the crowd that traveled with the Thompsons and supported them—the men who would stick with them now.

He wasn't armed, himself. It never had been his policy to wear his guns in town. He was in no position to do anything about what had happened. It wasn't his responsibility, anyhow. But he knew as he knelt there at the side of the dying man, that if someone didn't do something to challenge the Thompsons, the law would be forever dead in Ellsworth. The time had come to make an issue of the matter of law and order. A decision could be delayed no longer.

Here in Ellsworth, today, men would choose whether to live under a civilized code, or to live as savages. A champion was needed.

3 • MARSHAL FOR AN HOUR

Friends of Sheriff Whitney carried the dying man home, and Wyatt stepped into the entrance of Beebe's store. From there, he watched what was happening in the plaza. The Thompson brothers still were in front of Brennan's, but they wouldn't be there much longer. He could hear Ben shouting to his brother to grab a horse and ride. Ben, always more cool-headed than Bill, was looking for an easy way out of what had happened. If Bill got away, there wouldn't be anyone to arrest for the murder of the sheriff.

Someone touched him on the shoulder and he looked around to see Happy Jack Morco, an old Indian fighter, and at present, one of the deputy marshals here in Ellsworth. He stepped back to give Morco a better chance to see what was happening in the plaza.

"Take this rifle an' give me my shotgun," Ben shouted

at his brother. "An' grab a horse an' ride."

Wyatt moved up closer to Morco. "Step out there and get them while they're changing guns," he whispered.

But Morco shook his head. "Do you think I'm crazy? I'd face one man, or two, but there ain't no one who could face a crowd like those men backin' the Thompsons. I'm stayin' right here."

He was an old Indian fighter, and was a good hand with his guns, but he had no stomach for the fight that might lie ahead of him if he stepped out into the street.

Wyatt crowded forward. He saw Bill pick out a horse, swing into the saddle, and head slowly out of town. He heard the killer shouting back, daring anyone to come out and fight him.

No one did.

But even with Bill gone, there still was Ben Thompson and those with him to be reckoned with. Ben, now, was crossing to the Grand Central. His men trailed after him. Wyatt knew some of them. Cad Pierce, George Peshaur, Neil Kane, John Good. Gun fighters, every one. And there were others in the group who were equally famous as troublemakers.

Another deputy marshal, Charlie Brown, showed up at

the corner of the railroad shack, far across the plaza. Someone in Ben Thompson's crowd caught sight of him, shouted his name, and fired a shot that way. Then, every man in front of the Grand Central turned his gun on the railroad shack, behind which Brown had ducked. They pinned him down there, held him there, shouting and laughing and pumping shot after shot across the plaza.

Wyatt Earp still stood in Beebe's doorway, out of sight of Thompson's men, but able to see most of what was happening. It was clear to him that the display Thompson and his men were putting on was an announcement to Ellsworth that from here on, they would do as they wished. They had taken over the town and would run it as they saw fit. The marshal and his deputies might as well ride somewhere else. Here, they no longer would have any authority.

"I told you what it was like in Ellsworth, Mr. Earp," said a voice in Wyatt's ear.

He looked around and saw Jeff Crandall. He had found a place for himself and Jeff in a tent east of town, owned by a friend. And he had helped Jeff get a job at the cattle pens, where he should have been now.

"What are you doing here?" he growled.

"Everyone from the pens headed this way when the shooting started," Jeff answered. "I guess we wanted to see what was going on. Whew! Isn't it really something, Mr. Earp?"

"It's disgusting, humiliating, and it's liable to make me sick at the stomach if it goes on much longer," Wyatt answered.

Jim Miller, the mayor of Ellsworth, edged around the corner of Beebe's and entered the store, followed by Jack Norton, another of the town's deputies. Miller was deeply concerned over what had happened. He ordered Norton and Happy Jack Morco to place Ben Thompson under arrest.

"Not me," Morco said. "Any officer who stepped out on the street right now would get himself killed. We gotta wait till Ben Thompson cools down."

The other deputy nodded in agreement.

Miller stepped to the door. "Thompson," he shouted. "Ben Thompson! I call on you to surrender."

A derisive laugh was his only answer.

Miller mopped the perspiration from his forehead.

"You've got quite a police force," Wyatt said dryly.

Miller glared at him. "What concern is that of yours,

stranger? And who are you, anyhow?"

"I'm just a temporary citizen of Ellsworth," Wyatt answered. "But I don't much like the way the town's being run."

"And besides that, you talk too much to suit me," Miller snapped. "You don't even wear a gun."

"I wear guns," Wyatt said, "but right now, I don't have them with me. If I did, I would step out there in the street and put Ben Thompson under arrest."

Miller was desperate. He didn't like what was going on. He didn't like what Wyatt Earp had said to him. Any fool, he told himself, could talk big. Any fool could hand out advice as to what should be done.

He turned to where the two deputies, Morco and Norton, were standing. "You're fired," he shouted. "And so is the marshal, as soon as I can locate him. I've found us a new marshal."

He stepped up to Norton, ripped his badge from his vest, then swung around to Wyatt Earp. He said, "All right, mister. Here's your badge. You're now marshal of Ellsworth. Step back there in the store an' get some guns. Then go out and arrest Ben Thompson. I order it. Now, what have you got to say?"

Wyatt didn't have anything to say. He realized that in a way he had nagged the mayor into doing what he just had done. He almost had asked for the badge he now was holding. He stared at it for a moment, then pinned it on his shirt and walked deeper into the store.

Jeff Crandall caught up with him at the counter. The boy's face had a strained, startled look.

"You're not going to do it, are you?" he whispered. "You're not going to try to arrest Ben Thompson."

"Someone's got to do it," Wyatt shrugged.

He asked the clerk for two used .45's, cartridges, and two secondhand gun belts and holsters. He particularly wanted secondhand holsters, for a gun might stick in a new holster, and if he had to use his guns he wanted to be able to get them in a hurry.

The clerk showed him several secondhand guns. He picked two that suited his fancy, loaded them, and tested the way they were balanced. He picked two gun belts with worn holsters, buckled them around his waist, and adjusted the holsters to hang as he wanted them to.

All this time, everyone in the store was watching him. The faces he noticed looked more amazed than anything else. Amazed, probably, that anyone could be foolish enough to step out there on the street and attempt to arrest a man like Ben Thompson.

Jeff bit his lips. "I wish you wouldn't try it, Mr. Earp. That is—"

"Like I told you, Jeff, someone has to," Wyatt answered.

His muscles were beginning to tighten. His throat felt dry. He pictured in his mind the street he had to cross and every step he would have to take between here and the Grand Central. He pictured Ben Thompson, waiting there for him, and the crowd of killers ready to stand with Thompson in anything he might do.

He knew that if he stepped out into the street with a gun in his hand, he wouldn't live to take two steps. But he had a notion that if he left his guns in his holsters he might be able to cross the street. So long as he didn't touch a gun, those with Ben Thompson would leave it to Ben to start things. Ben was their leader. Ben was the one who had been roaring challenges at the town. If someone took the challenge and stepped out to meet him, no one else would interfere. At least, to begin with. What they might do later, no one could foretell.

With the holsters adjusted to his liking, Wyatt looked at Jeff and managed a smile. He said, "Jeff, you haven't yet run across any of the four men who killed your father, have you?"

"Not yet," Jeff answered.

"Then when you do, remember to ask the help of someone representing the law. The time is coming, Jeff, when the law will be respected. Anything anyone can do to hasten that day is a contribution to the welfare of the nation. Do you understand what I mean?"

"I think I do," Jeff said. "You mean, each time we support the law, we make it stronger."

"That's the idea," Wyatt nodded. "See you in a few minutes, Jeff."

He wasn't at all sure he would. He wasn't at all sure he would live to cross the street, or if he did, he wasn't sure what would happen when he got there. Ben Thompson had killed quite a few men in gun duels, and was supposed to be able to draw his guns with a lightninglike speed. That didn't trouble Wyatt. He was fast himself, probably as fast as Thompson. Or even faster. No, it wasn't Thompson alone that troubled him. It was Thompson's men he was worried about. It was what they might do after he and Ben had shot it out that troubled him. No man alone could face a trigger-happy crowd like the one that backed Thompson, and, in a gun fight, hope to live.

He walked to the door of the store, touched his guns to make sure they were free in their holsters, nodded to Mayor Miller, and stepped out on the porch. From there, he stared diagonally across the plaza toward the Grand Central.

Ben Thompson, standing in front of his men, saw him almost immediately, and turned to face him. Thompson still was holding the shotgun with which his brother had killed Sheriff Whitney. He swung it now so that it was leveled almost directly at Wyatt, the forefinger of his right hand on the trigger. A squeeze of that finger, and the gun would explode.

Wyatt tugged at his hat, then stepped into the street. As he started across the plaza he could feel the burning touch of the sun on his shoulders. His boots scuffed up a powdery dust. But these things seemed part of another world. For Wyatt Earp at that moment, nothing existed but the crowd in front of the Grand Central, and the man leading them. He saw nothing else, thought of nothing else.

He moved steadily ahead, one measured step after another. He was neither hurrying nor walking slowly. His arms swung loosely at his sides, his fingers now and then brushing the butts of his holstered guns. And he watched Ben Thompson like a hawk, watched for any move he might make.

He was halfway across the plaza now, close enough to the Grand Central to see Thompson's flushed and perspiring face. He took another dozen steps.

Thompson's voice whipped out at him suddenly.

"That's far enough, Wyatt. What do you want?"

"You, Ben," Wyatt answered.

He moved on.

Thompson's face had darkened, but a narrow, thoughtful look had come into his eyes. Or maybe it was a doubtful look. He could shoot down this brash young man who was crossing the street toward him. But while he was doing it, what would Earp be doing? He had heard of some of the shooting contests Wyatt Earp had entered, and of some of the almost incredible targets he had hit with his gun. Men said he was terribly fast and accurate.

"Wyatt!" he shouted. "Let's talk this over."

"We've got nothing to talk about, Ben," Wyatt answered. And he stopped.

Now was the time to make his play. Everything hung on what happened during the next few seconds, on his order and on Ben Thompson's decision.

"Ben," he said quietly, "toss your gun in the street and walk out here. Tell your men to keep out of this."

Thompson moistened his lips. He straightened. For an instant, Wyatt was sure he was going to defy him and that in another instant the plaza would echo to the sound of gunfire. But as the instant lengthened and as a dull, bleak look came into Thompson's eyes, he knew he had won.

"Toss your gun out in the street," he ordered again.

"And then what?" Thompson asked.

"Then you go to jail."

"At least that'll be a new experience," Thompson said wryly.

He tossed his shotgun into the street, lifted his arms above his head, and stepped forward.

There was a muttering rumble of discontent from those behind him. Wyatt hadn't yet touched his guns, but now, with a blazing speed, he whipped them up.

"You fellows back away from here," he snapped. "Now! Get a move on. *Pronto!*"

He sounded as though he meant it. The men in front of the Grand Central backed away. They were too many

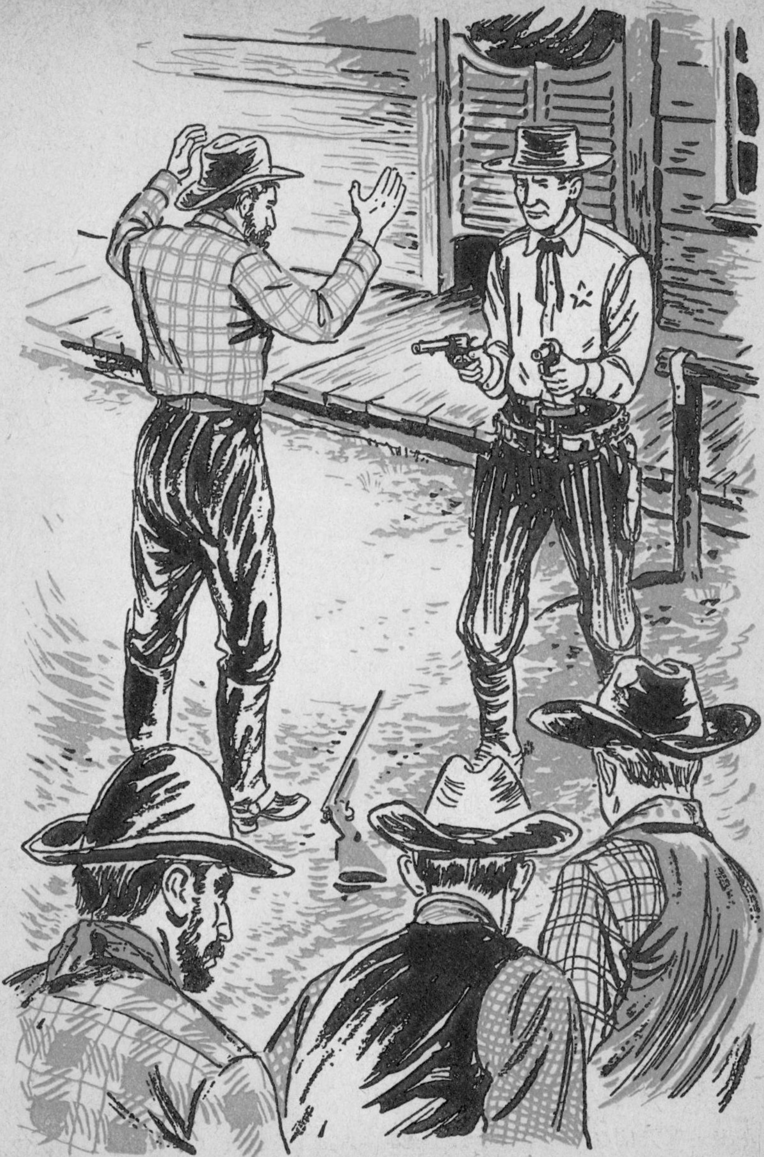

for Wyatt to have handled alone, but no one there wanted to be the first to go for his guns.

As they moved off, Wyatt holstered his guns and walked over to where Thompson was standing. He unbuckled the man's gun belt and, holding it, stepped back and said, "All right, Ben. Let's go."

"Where?" Thompson asked.

"To the jail," Wyatt told him.

Men had come out on the street again, and an amazed crowd stood watching as Wyatt led his prisoner across the plaza to Judge Osborne's court. They trailed after him, and soon hundreds of men were milling around outside the entrance to the judge's chambers.

In the forefront of the crowd were those who had stood with Thompson at the Grand Central, as well as a number of men who never had had any particular liking for the law, any kind of law. They spoke openly of a rescue.

There was other talk in the crowd, too. Some men were suggesting that Thompson be taken to the nearest tree and lynched.

Wyatt Earp wasn't afraid of a lynching, but he was seriously concerned about the attempt that might be made by Thompson's crowd to rescue him. And when some of the toughest of that group pushed into the courtroom, he climbed on a chair to face them.

"Outside," he ordered, pointing to the door. "Kane, Good, Pierce, Peshaur, get your men outside and keep them there. There'll be no rescue. There'll be no lynching."

"Better do as he says," Ben Thompson called. "He means it."

The armed men left the courtroom.

While this had been going on, the mayor, and Deputy Sheriff Hogue who had just returned to town, had been conferring with Judge Osborne. No one was quite sure on what charge Thompson could be tried. It was his brother who had killed the sheriff. But since Ben Thompson had helped his brother get away, it seemed reasonable to charge him with being an accessory.

The mayor, however, wasn't sure of the wisdom of this. Ben Thompson was a Texan, and Ellsworth was making a bid for the cattle trade from Texas. The mayor didn't want to do anything to offend the men who might drive their herds this way.

"I think he should be charged with disturbing the peace," the mayor declared.

"Guilty," the judge said quickly. "Twenty-five dollars fine."

Wyatt Earp couldn't believe what he was hearing. Here was a man who for days had terrorized the town of Ellsworth. He finally had been brought to the bar of justice, and was being dismissed with what amounted to no more than a slight slap on the wrist. To bring law to the lawless towns of the West, a courageous court was as necessary as fearless officers. The Ellsworth court didn't measure up to Wyatt's idea of what a court should be.

Thompson paid his fine. His guns were returned to him and he left the courtroom. Of course he wouldn't stay long in Ellsworth. Too many men here would remember how he had caved in when faced by young Wyatt Earp. His reputation had been damaged. He needed to go somewhere else and build it up again, preferably in a town where Wyatt Earp was not likely to visit.

The crowd in the judge's chambers thinned out. Wyatt hunted up the mayor. He handed back the badge the mayor had given him, and the guns he had chosen in Beebe's store.

"But I offered you the marshal's job," the mayor cried. "Don't you want it?"

"I certainly don't," Wyatt answered. "I risked my life to arrest a man you fined only twenty-five dollars. A marshal needs men to back him up. You don't seem to have any here."

He went outside, and halfway across the plaza was joined by Jeff Crandall. He glanced at the boy. "Do you like it here, Jeff?"

"It'll be a good town with you as marshal," Jeff said.

"But I'm not staying on as marshal. I'm riding west. Want to go with me?"

"You bet I do," Jeff cried.

"Then go get our horses. Pack our things."

He looked around the plaza. It was quiet again. The place had the look of an orderly town. Wyatt smiled. He had been marshal for only an hour, a rather tense hour, but he felt a deep satisfaction in what he had done. He felt he might like to try it again sometime.

A crowd was leaving the Grand Central. Thompson's crowd. He watched them mount their horses and ride away. Actually, and without knowing it, he was seeing more than the departure of a group of lawless men. He was witnessing the first signs of the death of an era.

Respect for law and order was coming to the West. It

would be born in violence and trouble and to the tune of blazing six guns. But it was on the way. And he, Wyatt Earp, would have a full share in making a place for it in the days to come.

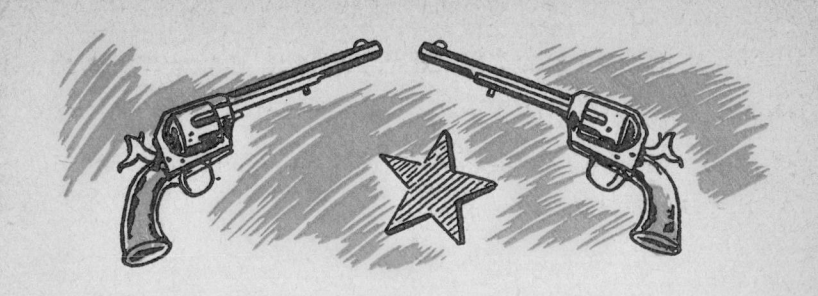

4 • THE WRONG SIDE OF THE LAW

Wyatt Earp hunted buffalo that winter, and Jeff went with him, joining the others in the party Wyatt headed. But they had to ride far north before they caught up with the great herd which once had roamed the endless plains of Kansas.

The trip was a success. It would pay off well in dollars earned, but by the time the season ended Wyatt had decided that this was his last year of buffalo hunting.

"Why?" Jeff wanted to know.

"We've driven the herd too far north," Wyatt replied. "By next year we would have to ride all the way to Montana to find enough buffalo to make the hunt worth-while."

"We could ride to Montana easily enough," Jeff said.

"Then will you pack the hides out to a railroad?" Wyatt asked laughing.

Jeff could see the point he was making. There were four separate parts to a buffalo hunt. First you had to find the buffalo, then kill them, skin them, and get the hides to a market. The last step was as important as any of the others. Too long a haul was impractical.

"So we'll be doing something else next year," Jeff said slowly. "What will it be?"

"Maybe we'll start our cattle ranch," Wyatt said. "How would you like that, Jeff?"

"It wouldn't be as exciting as a buffalo hunt."

"No, but there'll be more money in it for us. And a better life, Jeff. We'll take a look at the situation in Kansas as soon as we sell our hides. Cattle still are coming up the trail from Texas. The market may be better. It may pay us to invest what we have in Texas longhorns, and stake off a range and fatten them. We'll see."

They left it at that. Their plan was to sell the hides, then swing through Kansas and see what the situation was so far as the cattle business was concerned. One of Wyatt's brothers was in Wichita. They would go there first.

But a problem on Jeff's mind kept bothering him. He remembered what had happened in Ellsworth, the way

Wyatt had faced Ben Thompson and his crowd, and in effect, had driven them out of town. He had heard rumors that Thompson's crowd still were in Kansas, and he had heard, also, that they planned to get even with Wyatt if they ever had the opportunity.

What Wyatt would do if he had to face them again, Jeff didn't know. He shivered every time he tried to place himself in Wyatt's shoes. He had learned to handle a gun pretty well this winter. He was a dead shot with a rifle. But shooting buffalo and shooting men were two different things. Men could shoot back.

"I heard the other day that Ben Thompson still was in Kansas," he mentioned finally.

Wyatt shrugged. "I suppose he is."

"What if we run into him?"

"Why then, Jeff, we'll run into him."

"Do you reckon he'll cause trouble?"

"He might. Or again, he might not. We'll face that problem when we come up against it."

They rode on, and Wyatt, studying the boy's face, decided he knew what was bothering him. He said, "Jeff, let me tell you about Ben Thompson. I don't know him well, but I know a little about him. Ben is from Texas.

He fought in the Confederate army during the war and, like many other southerners, is bitter about the way the war ended. He's got to prove to himself, and to everyone else up here, that he wasn't whipped, that he's still as good as the next man."

"All Texans aren't like that," Jeff said quickly, remembering that he himself was a Texan.

"Of course not," Wyatt agreed. "But there are some men who fought in the war, men from both sides, who can't realize it's over. They still are ready to fight at the drop of a hat. And the situation in Kansas is ideal for it."

"How do you mean?"

"Men from the South drive cattle to Kansas which is a northern market. The cattle buyers are from the North. A good many Texans who come up here feel they are in an unfriendly country. If a town marshal orders them to behave, the natural thing to do is challenge him. And if a crowd of Texans can take over and control a town, it's like a military victory over the North."

"How long will such a condition go on?"

"It will go on until our town marshals get the courage to crack down and make the law something to live by."

"Crack down on the southerners?"

"Crack down on anyone who needs it. The war is over, Jeff. It isn't the North against the South any longer. This is just one country in which law and order must be upheld. In their hearts, men like Ben Thompson know that. They know they're acting like spoiled kids. In other words, half of their attitude is pure bluff."

"You mean Ben Thompson was bluffing when he marched back and forth in Ellsworth, daring anyone in town to do anything to him?"

"That's right, Jeff. He was bluffing. I don't mean he couldn't have shot at me, and maybe brought me down. But he didn't. When I called his bluff, he backed down. It wasn't because he was a coward. It was because he knew, deep down in his heart, that he couldn't stand up against the law."

"You think he'll back down when you face him again?"

"I don't know," Wyatt said. "I won't be looking for trouble when we ride through Kansas. It may be I'll meet Ben and we'll just talk, and nothing will happen. Or I may have to fight him. But, Jeff, you can't go through life dodging folks you might have trouble with. Let's not waste time worrying about men like Ben Thompson. They're not worth it."

This was sensible talk, and Jeff knew it, but he still couldn't help feeling uneasy about what might happen when they got to Wichita. And it was hard to understand why Wyatt seemed so unconcerned. Yet he did. Jeff was sure that if he had been in Wyatt's shoes he would have spent part of each day practicing his draw. Wyatt never even seemed to think of it.

It was late in May when Wyatt Earp and Jeff Crandall crossed the Arkansas River toll bridge and reined up at the west end of Douglas Avenue, in Wichita. They had been told that this year, Wichita, in all probability, would replace Ellsworth as the cattle capital of Kansas; that most of the herds of longhorns coming up the trail from Texas were Wichita bound. If that was true, this was where Wyatt would find the answer to his question as to whether or not to buy cattle and start ranching.

After a glance down Douglas Avenue, Wyatt turned to Jeff, and asked, "Well, Jeff, how does Wichita look to you?"

"About like Ellsworth," Jeff answered.

"You couldn't have said it better," Wyatt laughed.

He was right. Wichita, that year, looked like just another cattle town built on a mud flat close to a river. The buildings they could see along the main street were frame, many of them with false fronts and porches over the boardwalks. Hitching rails lined both sides of the street, and away from the business district was a clutter of dwellings of all types, some so hastily thrown up that a good wind would blow them over.

There were then, maybe twelve hundred people living in Wichita, but as the herds came up the trail from Texas, and as more cowboys and cattle buyers flocked to the town, the population would double, then double again. Wichita's great boom days were just starting.

"We'll stable our horses," Wyatt said, "then get a hotel room and look the town over."

There was a sudden blast of gunfire from down the street and, as they sat their horses, watching, a crowd gathered in front of one of the buildings.

"They'll never be able to keep peace in a town so long as men are allowed to wear guns," Wyatt muttered.

"But how would you stop men from wearing guns?" Jeff asked.

"I'd make it a law that a man had to check his guns as soon as he rode into town. Most hotels and stores have gun racks where guns can be checked."

"And if a man wouldn't check his guns?"

"Then I'd arrest him."

"Some Texans wouldn't like that. They're used to wearing their guns on the trail and wouldn't feel safe without them in town."

"They'd be safe if all men checked their guns. Jeff, men in the West started wearing guns to protect their herds, or to protect themselves from snakes. When he's in town, a man doesn't need a gun."

They stabled their horses, took a hotel room nearby, and after a casual survey of the town, Wyatt set out to locate his brother Jim, who had a job somewhere in Wichita. He wasn't greatly surprised when Jim told him Ben Thompson was here.

"He has the usual crowd with him," Jim said. "One of them, George Peshaur, boasts openly that he's going to kill you the day he sees you. Another, Joe Todd, has made the same statement."

"What about Ben?" Wyatt asked.

"So far as I know, Ben never has talked about what happened in Ellsworth. But he's the killer he always was. He's a man to watch, Wyatt. So are those who hang around him. You are the only man who ever made them back down. They can't forget such a thing."

"So I'm marked for a pine coffin, am I?"

"That's it, Wyatt."

"What about the law here in Wichita?"

"It's an easy-going law. It shuts its eyes to anything Thompson's crowd does."

"How long are towns like this going to put up with such a thing?"

"Who knows?" Jim shrugged. "What can you do about it, anyhow?"

"If I was the marshal here I'd do something about it, that's for sure," Wyatt answered.

He walked back to his hotel. The key wasn't at the desk where he had left it. Figuring that Jeff had returned to the hotel, he walked down the corridor to his room, opened the door, stepped inside, and came to an immediate stop.

It wasn't Jeff who was waiting for him. The man in his room was short, stocky, middle-aged, and had an ugly, bearded face. He held a gun in his hand, a gun pointed straight at the door.

Wyatt wasn't armed. He never wore a gun when in town. The man in the room he recognized as Joe Todd, who, according to his brother, had sworn to shoot him on sight. He didn't know Todd very well, didn't know how good he was with a gun, but from ten feet, the poorest shot in the world couldn't have missed him.

"Earp, I've been waiting for you," Todd said sharply. "I've been waiting for you since Ellsworth. Nice of you to come to Wichita and make it easy for me."

"I'm not armed," Wyatt said.

"Who cares about that," Todd snapped. "I'm going to kill you, Wyatt. I'm going to blow a hole through your chest wide enough to see through."

Wyatt leaned forward, resting lightly on the balls of his feet. He knew he couldn't cover the distance between himself and Todd before Todd could fire the gun. He could see only one encouraging thing in the situation. Todd seemed to want to talk, to boast a bit. If he could keep him talking, the chance might come to catch him off guard.

"How many men have you killed, Todd?" he asked quietly.

"That's none of your business, Earp."

"I don't believe you ever killed anyone," Wyatt said. "You're holding your gun as though you were afraid of it.

And you're sweating. You're not a killer. You're not even tough. You just hang around with a tough crowd hoping some of their courage will rub off on you. Well, it won't. After you've shot me, you'll start running. And you'll never stop."

"Shut up," Todd screamed.

Wyatt was leaning forward a little more, every muscle in his body tightened up. He prodded Todd again.

"Why should I shut up? A man who's about to be killed always is allowed to make a last statement. I'm making one—about a coward. A coward named Joe Todd."

A livid anger colored Todd's face. His hand, holding the gun, started shaking.

"I told you to shut up," he screamed again. "I told you—"

Wyatt waited no longer. He could see by the sharper look in Todd's eyes that the man had taken about all he could. It was his guess that Todd didn't have much courage, and the way he reacted to what had been said was proof that Wyatt's guess was right. His jabs at the man had dug under the skin, temporarily upsetting him. And right now was as good a chance as he might ever have to dive in at the gunman.

He tried it. He lunged forward, throwing himself at

Todd's knees. He heard the blast of the gun Todd was holding, but the bullet whistled above him. In another instant, his arms were wrapped around Todd's knees, and he had thrown the man to the floor.

Their struggle for the gun was quite brief. Wyatt Earp didn't weigh more than a hundred and fifty pounds. He looked thin and frail, but his muscles were like steel cords and he had perfect co-ordination of movement. He twisted the gun from Todd's hand, slammed the barrel across the side of the man's head, and then stood up.

"Get on your feet, Todd," he ordered.

Joe Todd got to his knees, then stood up. He backed to the wall and leaned there, seemingly grateful for its support. He was bug-eyed with fear. Perspiration trickled down the side of his face. His breath wheezed noisily through his throat. His jaw moved up and down as he made an effort to speak, but no words got past his lips.

"I ought to shoot you," Wyatt said. "Someday someone will."

Todd sucked in another noisy breath. "You mean—"

A crowd had gathered out in the hall. Someone knocked on the door which had blown shut after Wyatt stepped into the room. He ignored the knocking. He balanced

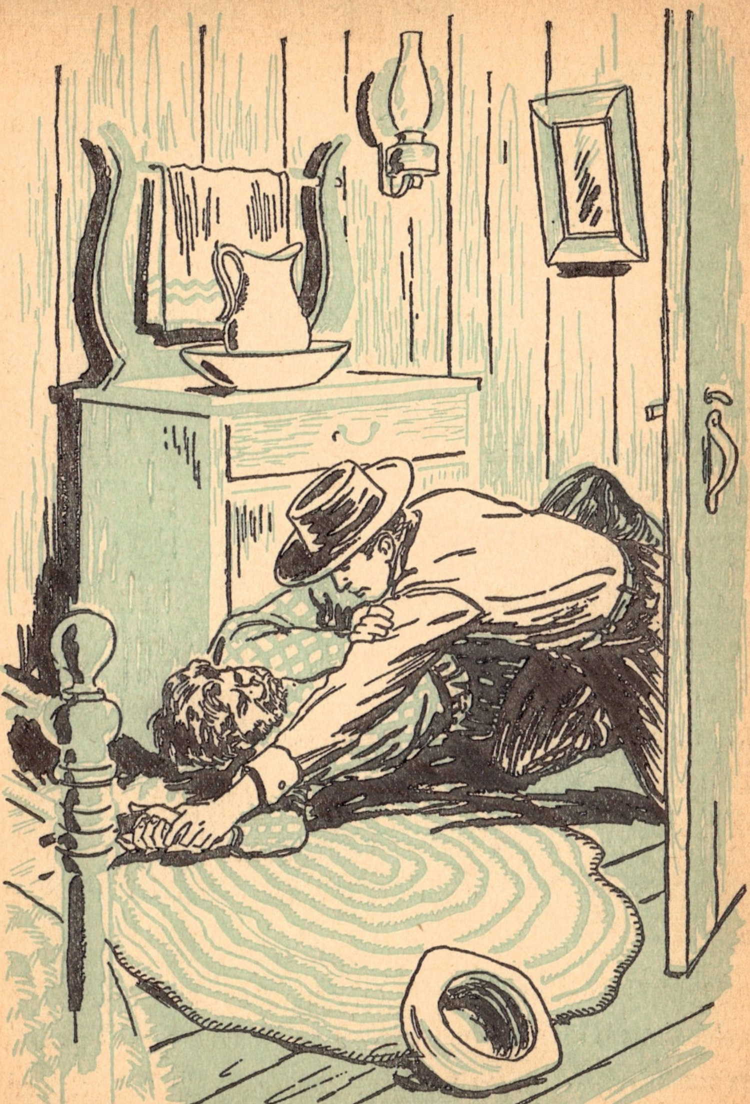

Todd's gun in his hand, watching the terrified man narrowly.

"You mean—" Todd gasped again.

"I mean this," Wyatt said. "I'm going to let you go, Todd, but when you walk out of here, fork your horse, ride out of town. And keep riding until you're out of Kansas. Don't chase back to Ben Thompson and think you'll be safe with him, for you won't be. If you stay in Wichita, I'll come after you. And if I do, you won't live very long. That's a promise."

Joe Todd moistened his lips. "I—I can go now?"

"Sure, you can go now," Wyatt snapped.

He tossed Todd's gun on his bed, walked forward, caught the man by the shoulders, and hustled him across the room. He opened the door and thrust him into the crowd outside. He wasn't very gentle about it.

"On your horse, Todd," he shouted, "and keep riding. Don't turn back."

He didn't explain to the men in the corridor what had happened. Some would know Joe Todd and would be able to figure out the essential details of what had occurred. A report on this would go back to Thompson, and to the others who had sworn to get him. It would make them even more angry, more determined. The future didn't look bright.

He closed the door to his room and started pacing back and forth. This trouble he had had with Joe Todd upset him more than he was willing to admit. It foreshadowed other experiences he would have if he stayed here. Maybe the thing he should do was see Ben Thompson and settle things with him, once and for all.

Through his window he heard the sound of a man shouting and of a boy's terrified screams. The noises seemed to come from behind the building. He left his room and walked down the corridor and out the back door.

Not a dozen steps away, a heavy-set man was struggling with a boy half a dozen years younger than Jeff. As he looked that way, the man threw the boy to the ground and started kicking him. The boy grabbed one of the big fellow's legs and the man sprawled down on top of him, then started beating him with his fists. The boy's screams grew louder.

A little more of this, Wyatt decided, and he would be fed up with Wichita, and the men who lived here. He stepped out in the yard, walked to where the man and boy were struggling, and pulled the man erect.

"Why not pick on someone your own size?" he demanded.

"If you want me to, I will," the man shouted, hardly glancing at him.

But the blow the man threw was well aimed. It smashed Wyatt squarely in the face, staggered him backward. He straightened up, moved in, and laced his fists at the man. One caught the fellow beautifully in the eye, another doubled him over. A third solid punch dropped him to the ground.

The man scrambled to his feet, took a startled look at Wyatt, then scurried away. The boy had climbed to his feet and started running the minute he had been freed.

Wyatt fingered his face. There was a slight swelling on his jaw where the man had hit him. He glanced at the few people who had drifted this way from the street, and among them saw Jeff Crandall, who hurried toward him.

"I seem to be getting mixed up in all sorts of trouble today," he said ruefully.

"You handled the fat man perfectly," Jeff answered. "What was the shooting in our room?"

"One of Ben Thompson's crowd came to see me, a fellow named Joe Todd. He ran out of courage, Jeff—

didn't have too much to start with."

"They say you let him go."

"Why not? If he leaves town, he's better off and we're better off than if he stayed."

"I should have stuck with you," Jeff said. "Are we going to be around Wichita long?"

"Why?"

"If we are, I might as well go to work. I can get a job at the cattle pens."

"We'll decide tomorrow," Wyatt said.

They started toward the hotel, then stopped. The fat man Wyatt had fought with was returning. With him was an average-sized man who wore a deputy marshal's badge on his vest.

"There he is," the fat man shouted, pointing at Wyatt. "I charge him with assault. I want you to place him under arrest."

The deputy stepped forward. "Are you Wyatt Earp?"

"I am," Wyatt nodded.

"Eb Black, here, charges you with assault."

"Did he explain what he was doing to the boy?" Wyatt asked.

"The boy worked for him and was being disciplined."

"Maybe so," Wyatt agreed, "but any time a two-hundred-pound man disciplines a boy with his fists, someone ought to interfere."

"You may be right at that," the deputy answered. "But I'll have to take you in. We'll see how the judge feels about it."

"You mean, I'm under arrest?"

"That's what I mean, Earp."

"You're not going to stand for it, are you?" Jeff asked under his breath. "Tell him to get going."

But Wyatt shook his head. "Jeff, a man's either for the law or against it. He supports and upholds it, or he fights it. You can't be on one side one day, and the other side the next day."

"You didn't do anything wrong."

"Then the judge will release me."

"What if he doesn't?"

"Why, in that case, the law has made a mistake. But if we really believe in it, then we respect the men hired to enforce it."

"Let's go, Earp," the deputy said gruffly.

Wyatt nodded. He believed what he had said, but it wasn't easy to submit to arrest, knowing that men like

Ben Thompson could get away with murder and not be troubled.

Of course things wouldn't go on like this. There would be a change made in the situation here in Wichita. There would have to be, if decent men continued to make this their home.

5 • TRAPPED

The judge couldn't be found. No one around his office knew where he had gone or when he would be back.

"So what do we do now?" Wyatt asked.

"I've got to hold you, I suppose," the deputy said, frowning. "There's a building we use now and then as a jail. I'll take you over there. You could break out of it, but I'm asking you not to, Earp."

"All right, I won't," Wyatt agreed. "But send someone to find the judge. I want to get this matter settled."

Jeff Crandall, who had come this far with them, left now to hunt for the judge. Wyatt and the deputy walked over to the jail.

It wasn't much more than a shack. How anyone could have been kept here very long against his will was a mystery. Wyatt decided, then and there, that another thing

Wichita needed was an adequate jail.

Half an hour later, Jeff came running up. He was out of breath and he looked frightened.

"They're coming, Wyatt," he shouted. "You'd better get out of here right away."

Wyatt came to the jail's doorway, and the deputy, who had been standing guard, joined them.

"Who's coming?" Wyatt demanded.

"Half the men in town, from all I hear," Jeff answered. "The man who had you arrested went from place to place, up and down Douglas Avenue. He boasted that you were in jail and asked where the judge could be found. No one seemed interested in the judge. One place where he stopped, some man said, 'Now's the time to get Wyatt Earp. Send word up and down the street that we're marching on the jail.' The crowd's gathering at Keno Corner."

Wyatt's eyes narrowed thoughtfully. It was in a building at Keno Corner that Ben Thompson hung out. He wondered if Ben could be back of this move to close in on him. It seemed quite possible. Or perhaps Ben was just riding along with the others. The way Wyatt had buffaloed the Texans in Ellsworth had stirred up a good many who never had seen him.

That, however, wasn't the problem he now was facing. If Jeff was correct in his report, quite a crowd would be heading this way in the next few minutes. A good many in the crowd might be trailing along with the others, but some among them would be men who had been at Ellsworth, and who would be glad of a chance for a safe shot at him.

"Find my brother, Jeff," he ordered brusquely. "Tell him what's happening."

"There won't be time for that," Jeff answered. "Here they come."

He was right. A crowd of booted and spurred men had turned off of Douglas Avenue and were headed this way. Their shuffling feet kicked up a cloud of dust. Wyatt could hear the lifting boom of their voices. Several had started singing, as though this was more of a sporting event than anything serious.

"I'll go get some help," the deputy said nervously.

He turned and hurried off.

Wyatt glanced from side to side. There was no back way out of the jail. He could leave now by the front door, but not without being seen. The nearest cover was a good distance away. He could try to get there. He might make it. But there was a good chance he wouldn't. If he left here and raced for cover, half the men headed this way might open fire. He would be cut down like a rabbit.

"They're not after you, Jeff," he said quickly. "Go find my brother. I may be able to stall them for a while."

Jeff shook his head. "No. I'll stay here."

Wyatt glanced at him. The boy still looked pale, frightened, but his lips were closed in a tight, stubborn line, and his fists were clenched. During the past few months, Wyatt had come to know him well, and had grown fond of him. He knew that Jeff felt a certain loyalty toward him, but he never before had known how deep it went.

"Jeff, go find my brother," he said again. "That's an order."

"I'm not working for you now," Jeff answered. "You can't give me orders. I'm staying here."

"And what good do you think that will do?"

"I don't know," Jeff admitted. "But I'm staying."

"Then get inside," Wyatt growled. "If they start shooting, drop down on the floor."

Jeff entered the jail. Wyatt stood waiting in the doorway, which still was partially open. The crowd headed this way now was close enough so that he could recognize some of the men. He saw Peshaur, Brady, Sloan, Rockhaven, and several others whom he remembered from Ellsworth, but he couldn't find Ben Thompson anywhere in the front ranks. He stepped back into the jail and slammed the door shut. He looked around for something to brace against it, but there was nothing available.

"Hey, Earp!" shouted a voice from the crowd. "Earp, come on out. We want you!"

"Then come in and get me," Wyatt answered. "But I'll break the head of the first man through the door."

"There's too many of us for you, Earp," the voice shouted. "Make it easy on yourself. Come on out."

"Why don't you come in?" Wyatt replied.

He heard the crack of a rifle shot and dropped quickly to the floor, glancing at Jeff who was sprawled out near him. He said, "Sorry, Jeff. You should have left here while you could."

"Who's complaining?" Jeff answered.

Other shots splintered through the building, most of them high. But a few were low. And soon, more of the shots would be cutting lower.

Wyatt rolled to the side wall of the building, motioning for Jeff to do the same. How long he had until some chance shot would reach him, he didn't know. More than anything else, he felt angry. Angry that such a thing as this could happen. Angry that mob rule could take over in a town, and that two unarmed men, cornered and helpless, could be shot to death, for it looked like that was what was going to happen.

The firing thinned out, stopped. Wyatt raised his head. He strained his ears, listening. He couldn't hear what was being said outside but he could imagine at least a part of the talk that would be going on. The men out there were wondering if their shots had reached him. And some, probably, were worrying about what soon might happen. On several occasions, from what his brother had told him, the citizens here in Wichita had banded together against the Texans. At no time had there been open conflict between the two groups, but the threat of it hung over the town, and an outbreak like this could blow the lid off.

He crawled toward the door.

"Where are you going?" Jeff whispered.

He looked around. "I want to see what's happening out there. Stay where you are, Jeff."

He reached the door, pushed it open an inch or two, and looked outside. The crowd from Keno Corner was gone.

He couldn't believe it, but it was true.

A voice from the side of the building reached his ears. "Earp? Earp, are you all right?"

He got to his feet, opened the door, and looked out. The deputy, who had left here before the firing started, had returned, and with him were a dozen or more grim-faced townsmen, among them his brother Jim.

"They quit firing, backed off, soon as they saw us headed this way," Jim Earp said. "We'll have a real showdown with them sometime, but they didn't want it now."

"Ben Thompson wasn't with them," Wyatt said.

"No. Nor Mannen Clements. If they had been here it might have been a different story."

"You mean Mannen Clements is in Wichita?" Wyatt asked.

"He's camped on a creek near here, holding his cattle for a better price. He spends a lot of his time in town. Quite a bunch of riders with him, all hard men, proud they're Texans, and ready for an argument any time."

Wyatt's eyes narrowed thoughtfully. Mannen Clements, in a way, was a more dangerous character than Thompson or any of Thompson's crowd. He was an important Texas cattleman, whose word carried a lot of weight with others who came up the long trail. In addition to that, he had acquired quite a reputation as a gun slinger. Wichita might be glad to run Thompson out of town, for Thompson was nothing more than a gambler. But if they bucked Mannen Clements, he might drive his cattle to some other shipping point, and persuade others to do likewise.

"You might as well hear the worst of it." Jim Earp continued. "I got word only a few minutes ago that John Wesley Hardin's here, too."

Wyatt took a deep breath. John Wesley Hardin probably was the most dangerous man who ever rode up the trail from Texas. Wichita was in for some tough days.

He glanced at the deputy. "Do I have to stay here in jail and be shot down like a cornered rat?"

"You'd be smart if you got out of town," the deputy answered. "We chased that crowd off, but every one of them will be on the lookout for you from now on."

"Then how about letting me get somewhere safe? And how about loaning me your guns, so I can get there?"

The deputy hesitated, then nodded, and unbuckled his gun belts. "Leave these for me at the hotel where you are staying. I can get other guns uptown."

Wyatt buckled one of the holstered guns around his

waist. He handed the other belt to Jeff.

"What do you reckon you'll be doing, Wyatt?" his brother asked. "Where will you be riding?"

"Who said anything about riding anyplace?" Wyatt answered. "We weren't brought up to run, Jim. You ought to know that quite well."

"Then, where are we going from here?"

Wyatt shook his head. "You go back to your job. Let me work this out myself. I'm the man Thompson's crowd is after."

"But—"

"No, Jim," Wyatt said stubbornly. "Leave it up to me."

He motioned to Jeff, turned away, and started circling back to the hotel where he and Jeff had taken a room. They kept away from the main street. Wyatt had no intentions of running into a shooting scrape if he could avoid it. He did have a plan in mind. It was rather vague, and where it would lead he didn't know, but he was thinking that his next step should be to confront Ben Thompson, and find out just where Thompson stood, so far as he was concerned. And how far Thompson meant to go.

But several other things were to happen before he would have a chance to face Thompson. As he and Jeff were heading toward their hotel, a man hurrying after them caught up with them.

"Earp," the man said, "the mayor wants to see you. Right now."

"The mayor wants to see me?" Wyatt said, grinning at Jeff. "How wonderful, for I want to see the mayor. And when I do I want to ask him if he's proud of the town he's running. Come on, Jeff. Let's go talk to the mayor."

6 • THE MARSHAL OF WICHITA

That year, Jim Hope was mayor of Wichita. He was a forceful, determined man, well respected in most quarters. He had a difficult job, and he knew it. He wanted to hold the cattle trade, and, at the same time, maintain law and order in the streets.

Thus far, the task had been hopeless. The drive up the trail from Texas took several months. When the cowboys were paid off, and rode into town with their pockets full of money and ready to celebrate, it was hard to hold them down.

In the past, the cow towns in Kansas had known two kinds of marshals. One was the easy-going type, who shut his eyes to everything that was going on and who managed to be somewhere else whenever there was trouble. The other type was the hired killer, who tried to maintain order through fear, who swaggered through the town as a bully. Wichita had had several marshals of the killer type. None had lasted very long. A man who lived by his guns sooner or later was challenged by someone who was better, or was shot in the back by a friend of someone he had killed.

Neither type of marshal had proven satisfactory. The killer marshal made too many enemies, and didn't last long. The rabbit-type marshal failed to maintain law and order. Hope was looking for a man of different qualities, a man who could maintain peace in the streets without having to enforce it at the point of a gun. He needed a strong man whom the cowboys would respect, but who would use his gun only in an emergency. He was afraid the search for such a man was hopeless, yet he knew that such a man had to be found.

Like everyone else along the border, he had heard of Wyatt Earp's brief experience as marshal of Ellsworth. There, Earp had faced a crowd of Texans, and without firing a shot had arrested their leader. Another time, facing another crowd, such a man might be shot down. It might not be possible to repeat, in Wichita, what had happened in Ellsworth, but it seemed to Hope that if Earp had pulled the trick once, he might be able to do it again. At least it was worth while to take the chance.

This was in Hope's mind when he sent for Earp, although Wyatt didn't know it. He still was angry when he and Jeff stood face to face with the mayor.

"Fine town you've got here," Wyatt said. "I suppose you know what just happened?"

"Yes, I've heard about it," Hope admitted.

"Then why not hire a marshal who's not afraid of the job?"

"You, Mr. Earp?"

"I'm going into the cattle business."

"You can do that later. How would you like to be marshal of Wichita?"

"You mean that, Mayor?"

"The job's yours if you'll take it."

Wyatt took a deep breath. He glanced at Jeff, but without seeing him. Taking a job as marshal in Wichita had been the farthest thing from his mind when he came here. He never had guessed it would appeal to him, yet it did. Since his brief experience as a law officer in Ellsworth, he had done a lot of thinking about the problem of law and order along the frontier. He didn't see why it wasn't possible to run a town where a cowboy could have a good time

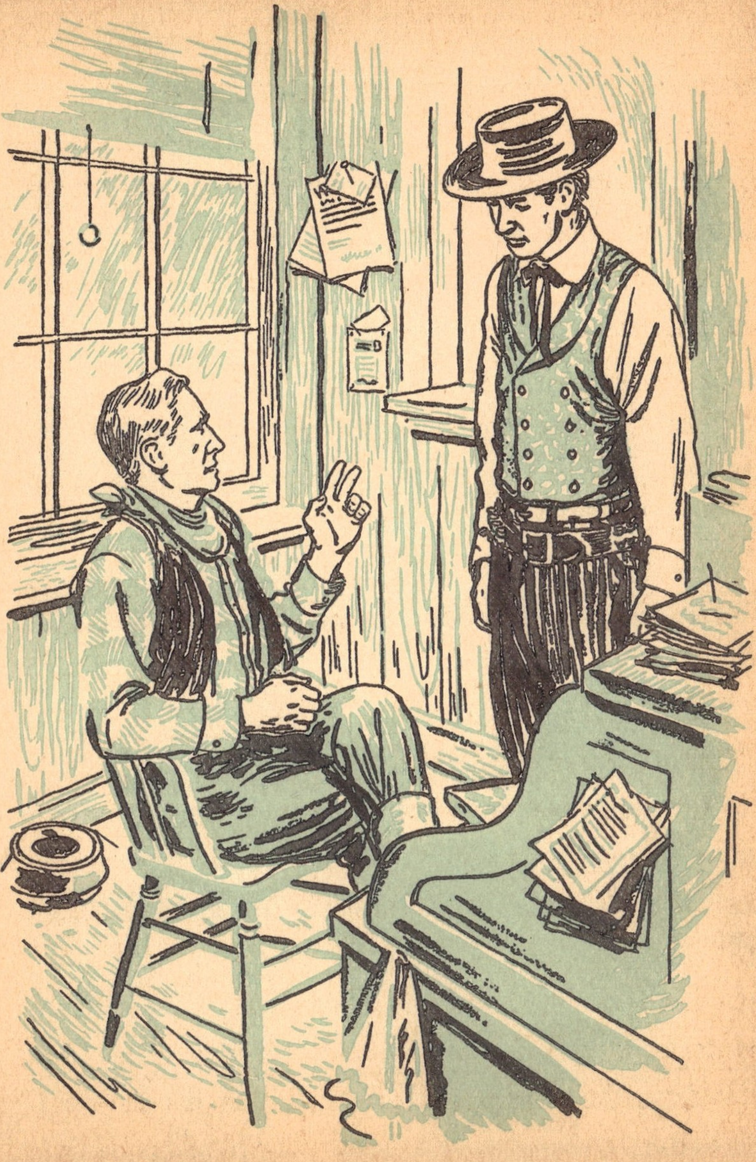

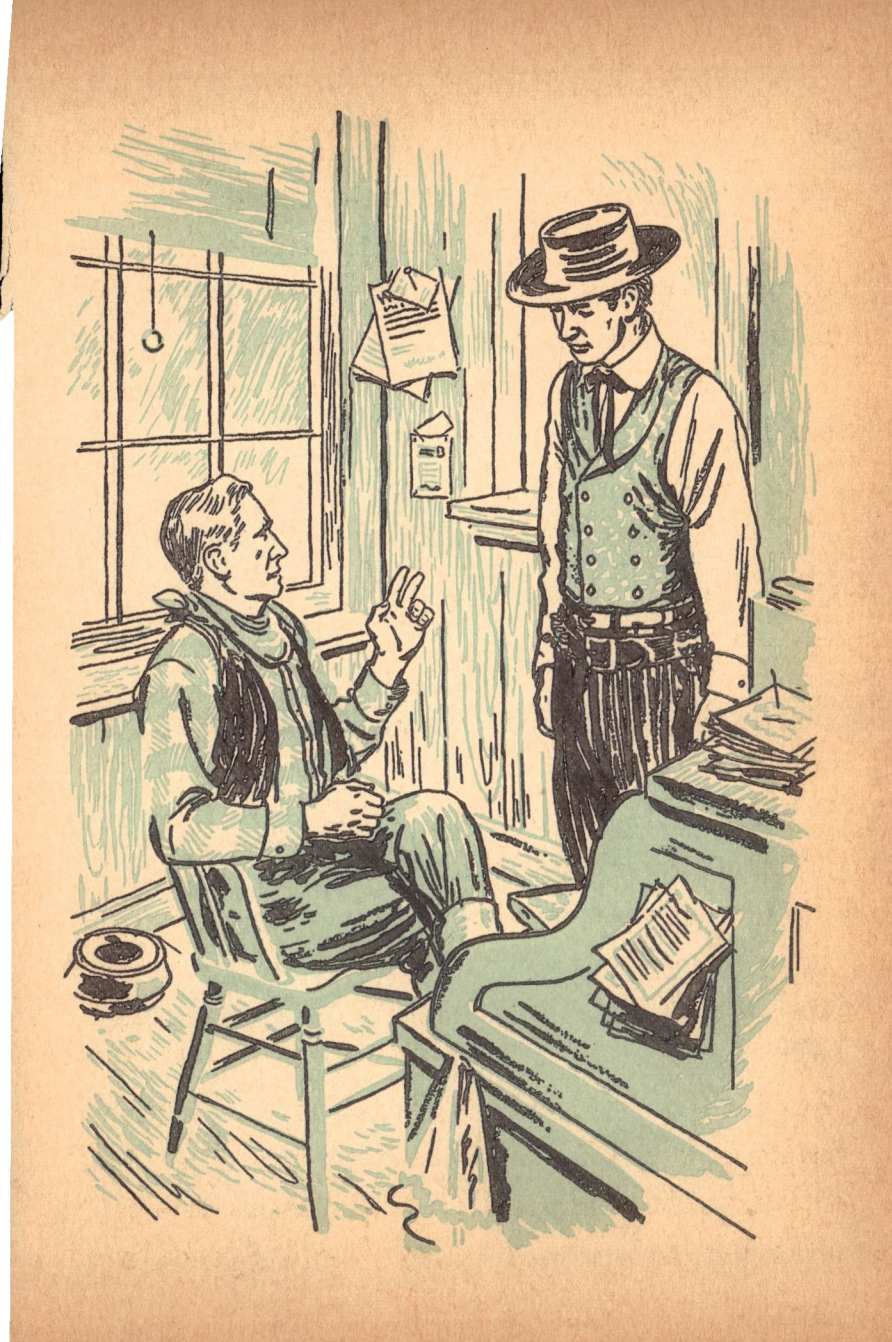

after his long trip on the trail without shooting up the town and everything in it.

And another thing interested him. He had a score himself to settle with the Texans. He was going to have to face them anyhow, whether or not he took the marshal's job.

"Will you stand back of me if I pin on the badge?" he asked bluntly.

"I won't stand back of a killer."

"I'm not a killer," Wyatt snapped. "I never, in any quarrel I've had, drew a gun if I could avoid it."

"Then I'll stand back of you, all the way."

Wyatt again glanced at Jeff. He said, "Jeff, how about it?"

"You can do it if anyone can," Jeff said.

Wyatt nodded. "Give me the badge, Mayor."

Hope pinned a badge on his vest. "This is only a deputy's badge," he mentioned. "But you'll have all the authority you want. Where do you intend to start?"

"I don't know," Wyatt said. "But one of the first things I'll want is a jail that can be locked up, and that will hold a man I put there."

"I'll put a new door and new lock on the jail in the next hour," the mayor promised.

"And two things more. I want to talk to the other deputies, soon as they can be brought together. And I want the word sent out, along Douglas Avenue and Main Street, that I've pinned on a badge."

"Wichita will hear of it soon enough," the mayor said. "Never worry about that."

Jim Hope was right. The word of Wyatt Earp's appointment as a deputy marshal ran up and down Douglas Avenue like wildfire. It spread along Main Street, down to the cattle pens, and out through the shacks across the toll bridge.

It created a sharp excitement. In Pryor's, a wager was posted that Wyatt Earp wouldn't last until midnight, and in the Texas House, at Horse-Thief corner, three men argued as to which of them should have the honor of shooting it out with Wichita's newest law officer. A man named Brady won the debate. He cleaned and oiled his guns and started patrolling Douglas Avenue, waiting for Earp's appearance.

There was another meeting in the Keno House. Ben Thompson was there, and George Peshaur, John Good, Neil Kane, and several others.

"I say we ought to get him, and the sooner we get him the better," Peshaur declared.

"I agree," John Good nodded.

Ben Thompson scowled. "I think we'd be wise to let things ride, and see what happens. This Wyatt Earp is a tough man."

"That sounds like yellow talk to me," Peshaur cried.

Thompson jerked to face him. "Say that again, and when you do, reach for your gun."

George Peshaur counted himself a brave man, but he wasn't anxious to test his gun skill with Ben Thompson. He knew how quickly Thompson could whip a gun up and fire it. He gulped, and looked down at the floor.

"I didn't mean it, Ben," he mumbled. "Folks like you and me have got to stick together. It's just that ever since Ellsworth—"

"Shut up about Ellsworth," Thompson roared. "We've got a good thing here. We're making money. I've got a notion Wyatt Earp won't bother us if we don't bother him, so I say, let someone else look after him."

Peshaur shrugged. He made no other answer, but in his own mind he had decided to take care of Wyatt Earp at the first opportunity.

A third group was disturbed at the appointment of the new deputy. At the cowboy camp out on the creek below Wichita, the Clements brothers, John Wesley Hardin, the Dixons, and several others discussed what ought to be done. They reached no decision that night, but from those men out on the creek, at a later date, would come the greatest threat to the new order in Wichita.

In the mayor's office, Wyatt belted on his guns, one to hang at his right hip, one at the left. He talked with the other deputies, whom the mayor had called. His instructions to them were simple, and to the point. He didn't want any shooting if it possibly could be avoided.

"Men who don't keep in line," he said grimly, "we will arrest. They will be lined up in Jewett's court the next morning. They will be fined, warned, and set free. From now on, we'll not stand for anyone shooting up the town. All guns are to be checked."

"There's no law requiring that," the mayor said uneasily.

"Then pass one," Wyatt said. "And until you can, send out the word that one sure way for a man to get in trouble in Wichita is to wear a gun."

After the meeting, he and Jeff had supper, then walked

down the street to their hotel.

"Do you really think you can enforce a law like that?" Jeff asked. "A law requiring cowboys to check their guns when they come to town?"

"We've got to," Wyatt said. "It's the key to the entire problem. A man wearing a gun can kill another. A crowd of men carrying guns can terrorize a town. Without guns, a man has only his fists. You can't hurt anyone very much with your fists."

"I wish I was a year or two older," Jeff growled. "I'd like to be with you in this."

"You are with me, I hope, Jeff."

"I mean, I'd like to be wearing a badge."

"In a year or two, you can, if you still feel you want to. Towns will always need good men to enforce the law."

Wyatt was deliberately waiting for several hours to pass, so that word of his appointment could sift up and down the streets of the town. He knew it would be resented by Ben Thompson's crowd at the Keno House, and by others who looked on him as a natural foe of the Texans. And he knew that his authority would be tested. The next hour or two would be critical in the life of Wichita. He might have greater troubles later on, but unless he managed things rather well in the next hour or two, he might not be here later on.

Jimmy Cairns, one of the other deputies, joined him at the hotel. Cairns, a quiet, soft-spoken man, looked very worried.

"There's talk along the street that you won't last out the night as a deputy," he reported. "I don't know who is going to call you, or where it will happen, but I'm sure something's been planned."

"You think they're ready?" Wyatt asked.

"I think they've been waiting since before dark."

"Then let's not keep them waiting any longer. We'll walk down Douglas Avenue, then along Main Street. If they don't make their play out in the open we'll start visiting the joints, one after another. You keep with me, but when they make their move, let me handle things."

"It's your party," Cairns said. "But don't forget that I'm along."

"You don't need a third man, do you?" Jeff suggested.

Wyatt turned to grip his hand. He said, "Jeff, you would do better as a third man than almost anyone I know. But tonight, two of us will be enough. See you tomorrow."

They left the hotel and started down Douglas Avenue,

Wyatt walking on the outside, Cairns next to the frame buildings, his right hand hooked in his belt, close to his gun. It was a dark night, but enough light came through the store and shop windows to thin the shadows. Saddled horses were at the hitching rails, and here and there stood groups of men while others passed back and forth across the street, or strolled up and down it. Some wore guns, some didn't.

Ahead of them there was a sudden blast of firing, then the high sound of excited voices. Cairns started to hurry forward, but Wyatt caught his arm. "We'll get there. Take it easy."

A man raced past them on a horse, streaking out of town. He was followed by two others who were firing at him, trying to bring him down.

"The second men are friends of someone shot down by the first," Wyatt guessed. "If gun-toting wasn't allowed, the shooting wouldn't have happened."

He was right in his estimate of the situation. What had happened farther down the street was but another incidence of the lawlessness which plagued the town. It had nothing to do with his recent appointment as a deputy marshal. The personal test which he was expecting awaited him at the next corner.

Luke Brady had paced the avenue until his legs were weary. Again and again he had loosened the gun in his holster. He was a stockily built man, still in the late thirties. This spring, he had driven five hundred longhorns north from Texas, bringing them here as part of a larger herd owned by Mannen Clements. He was holding them now, for a better price than at present was being offered.

Brady was nearly out of money, his nerves were on edge, and he was uncertain what to do in the immediate future. He had nothing, personally, against the new deputy, but it was in his mind that if he took care of Earp, he might stand a better chance of getting a loan from Clements. In addition to that, he had a notion he was as good with his guns as anyone riding for Clements. Here was a dramatic way to prove it, and to establish himself as a man to be reckoned with.

But by now he was tired and impatient, and he was beginning to feel the strain of the passing hours. He lounged against the wall of a corner hotel, anxiously watching everyone who passed.

Two men coming along the avenue toward him suddenly caught his attention. Both wore badges on their vests. He noticed that as they passed the first lighted hotel window. One man he recognized—Jimmy Cairns. The other he didn't know. The other was tall and slender. He had heard Wyatt Earp was tall and slender.

Every muscle in his body stiffened. He touched his holstered gun once more, making sure it wasn't bound. An immediate plan of action ran through his mind. He would let the two men pass him, then, an instant later, step out and shout for Earp to turn around and draw. This would give him a safe advantage, and if Earp saw that, and refused to draw, he would pistol-whip him out of town.

He stood waiting, scarcely breathing as the two men drew closer.

Wyatt had been in no hurry as they came down the avenue. He had refused to hurry on with Cairns when they had heard shooting up ahead, out of the simple conviction that somewhere along here, his authority would be challenged. He wanted to see and anticipate that challenge, not run into it blindly.

His eyes made a constant survey of the avenue as they moved along it. He paid particular attention to the groups standing in one place, and to men standing alone. Those moving up or down the street apparently had a definite destination in mind, and were less likely to be concerned with him.

He noticed Brady as they came to the hotel, and as they drew nearer he could sense the tension in the man's body. Brady no longer was lounging against the wall of the building. He stood erect, slightly hunched over. His right hand was curved as it might curve to grab a gun, although Brady must have been unaware of this. And he was wearing a holstered Colt.

The man wasn't watching Wyatt and Cairns. He might not have noticed the deputies coming down the street. He might be innocently waiting on the corner, but as they reached him, Wyatt came to a sudden decision. He stopped and turned to face the man, and a step or two farther on, Cairns stopped and looked back.

"Hello there, mister," Wyatt said. "Waiting for someone?"

Brady sucked in a quick breath. "What's it to you if I am?"

"Merely curious," Wyatt said. "Don't they have a gun rack where you're staying—a place where you can check your guns?"

Brady felt a surge of courage. "I'm from Red River," he shouted. "I wear my guns wherever I go. I use 'em whenever I want to. Like this!"

His right hand slashed quickly back to his holster, clutched his gun, and whipped it up with all the speed he had.

By every standard and code of the West, Wyatt would have been perfectly justified in matching his own speed against Brady's. Instead, he stepped forward, lifting his right arm in front of his body, then cut down in a sideways blow that slammed against Brady's wrist and gun, turning the gun aside.

He heard the blast of a shot as the gun went off, the bullet plowing into the boardwalk, and as that sound was echoing in his ears, his left fist exploded in Brady's face, driving the man back against the building.

A hoarse, startled cry broke from Brady's throat. Wyatt stepped in and hit him twice more, then stood back. Brady's knees folded. His gun slid from his hand. He collapsed to the boardwalk, too dazed to understand what had happened.

Cairns stooped over and collected his guns, then looked at Wyatt.

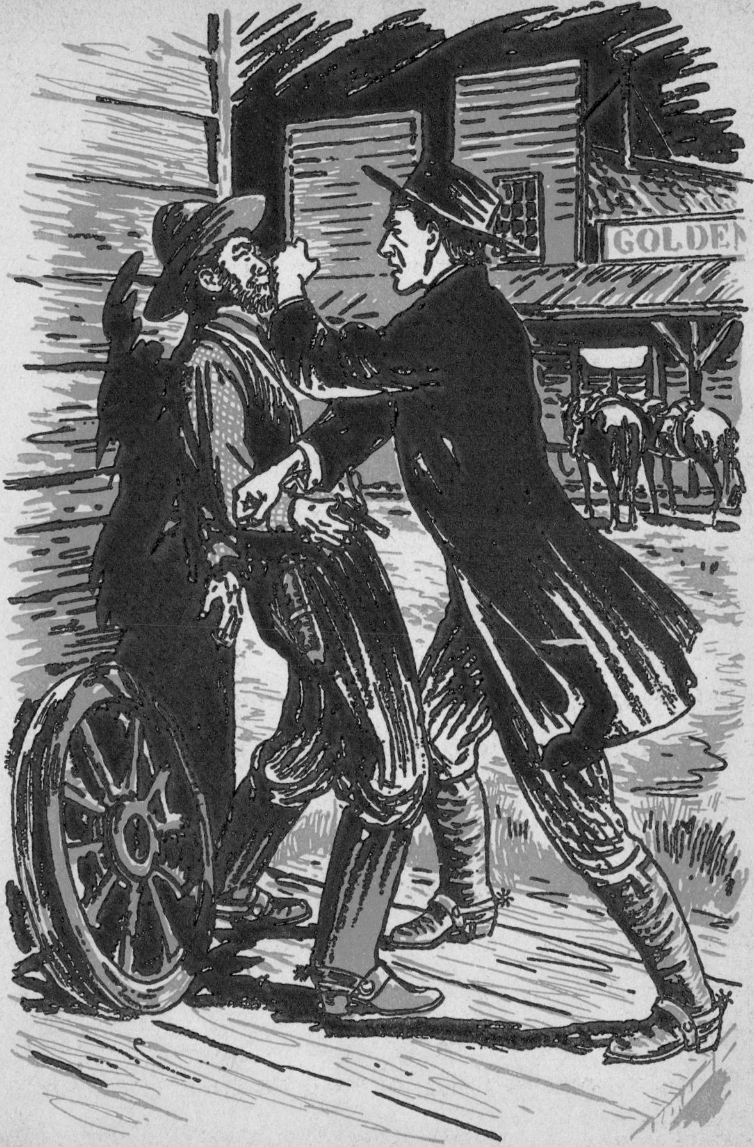
GOLDE

"Take him to the jail," Wyatt said quietly. "Lock him up. He can face Judge Jewett in the morning."

A crowd had collected to witness this first arrest to be made by the new deputy.

"What will the charge be?" Cairns asked.

"Make it drunkenness," Wyatt answered. "Any man who tries to draw his gun on a deputy here in Wichita must be either drunk or crazy. Who is he?"

"He rode here with Mannen Clements," someone in the crowd offered. "His name is Brady. Clements isn't going to like it that you arrested him."

"Too bad," Wyatt said. "Lock him up, Cairns."

"And where will I find you again?" Cairns asked.

"At the Keno House," Wyatt answered. "I'm going there to have a talk with Ben Thompson."

He glanced at the crowd which had gathered. It wasn't a large crowd, but here and there were men who had ugly, antagonistic looks on their faces. He decided, quite abruptly, that it was time to make a public declaration of his principles. It might save trouble. Of course, there was a chance he couldn't enforce the rules he set down, but if he couldn't, then he didn't deserve the honor of wearing a lawman's badge.

"I see that some of you fellows are wearing guns," he remarked. "Go to your hotels, or some store, and check them. From now on, a man who wears his gun in town is headed for trouble."

"There ain't no law against wearing guns," someone shouted.

"But there will be," Wyatt said. "And until there is you'd be wise to play it safe."

He turned then and started on down toward the Keno House on Keno Corner. He finally was going to have his talk with Ben Thompson. Talk or fight. He wasn't sure which.

7 • THE GATHERING STORM

The Keno House was a two-story frame structure in the heart of Wichita. Ben Thompson had his rooms and office on the second floor. He was there when Wyatt Earp came in from the street. One of his men hurried quickly up the stairs and told him Earp was below, asking for him.

"Tell him where I am," Thompson answered.

"You want some of us to come up with him?" the man inquired.

"What for?"

"I thought—"

"Suppose you let me do the thinking," Thompson said angrily. "Tell Earp where I am. And don't get any funny ideas about making a hero out of yourself."

The man left the room, and after he was gone Thompson started pacing back and forth, from wall to wall. He thought he knew why Earp had come. Since they were in the same town and since Earp had taken a deputy's badge, it was inevitable that they should face each other. This was particularly true in view of what had happened in Ellsworth.

His gun belts were lying on his desk. He buckled them on, then checked the loading in each gun, aware of the quiet excitement stirring in his body. Although he knew why Earp had come, he wasn't quite sure what would happen when they met. He didn't want to have to match his six-gun skill with the new deputy, but there might be no way to avoid it.

A knock sounded on the door. Thompson swung to face it. He called, "Come in."

Wyatt Earp stepped into the room. He noticed, almost instantly, that Thompson was wearing his guns. That might hold some meaning for him, or might not. He wasn't sure.

"Hello, Ben," he said quietly.

"Hello, Wyatt. I'm sorry to see you wearing that badge."

"Why?"

"I'm afraid it means the end of the good days in Wichita."

"No. It means the beginning of good days," Wyatt said.

"That depends on what a man calls good."

"Law and order are good."

"Not in my business."

"Then your business will have to go."

"Is that an order to close up?"

"Not yet," Wyatt said. "If you run an orderly house, we'll have no trouble. I want no shooting. If men have got to fight, let them fight with their fists. Tell the men who work for you to quit wearing guns on the street, and in your game rooms below."

"Then what do I do if I have trouble with some punch-happy cow hand?"

"Take the case to Judge Jewett's court."

"I never in my life depended on a court," Thompson flared.

Wyatt shrugged and then grinned. "Times are changing, Ben. A smart man changes with them. You can start now by unbuckling the gun belts you're wearing and putting them away."

Now, if he was going to do it, was the time to challenge Wyatt's authority. Thompson could feel his muscles tightening. He stared into the eyes of the man facing him. They were as blue and as cold and as unyielding as they had been that day in Ellsworth.

"Wyatt," he said abruptly, "if I reach for my guns both of us will die."

"Probably," Wyatt admitted.

"Don't you want to live?"

"Sure. Don't you?"

Thompson made no immediate answer, but he knew what his answer was going to be. Wyatt Earp wouldn't back down from the stand he had taken, even at the cost of his life. Of that, Thompson was positive. The tension in his body slipped away. He turned and walked toward his desk, suddenly feeling older. He unbuckled his gun belts and laid them there.

"What else do you want me to do?" he asked tiredly.

"Tell the men who work for you to stop wearing guns when in town," Wyatt answered.

"Some may not do it."

"Make them!"

"Anything else?"

"Run an orderly establishment here at the Keno House. Don't make my job any harder than it already is."

Ben Thompson nodded. He sat down at his desk and a wry smile crossed his face.

"Wyatt," he said slowly, "you've got guts. Half of the reason I didn't throw my gun on you in Ellsworth was that I envied the courage you showed in walking across the street to face me. I don't know whether or not you can tame Wichita, but I'll give you this promise. I won't stand in the way."

Wichita had entered upon a new era. It didn't take men long to realize that, although some learned it the hard way. Cowboys still rode into town wearing their guns, but if they didn't check them promptly at the first place they stopped, before an hour had passed, they found themselves under arrest, charged with drunkenness, or disturbing the peace, or vagrancy. Until a law was on the books prohibiting the wearing of guns in town, any other charge would serve. This wasn't strictly legal, but it was effective.

There were some, of course, who resented and resisted arrest, and there were several men who rode to Wichita for the definite purpose of shooting it out with the new deputy. Jeff Crandall, who got into the habit of roaming the streets at night, saw Wyatt handle three such men in one evening. Two, who tried to draw on him, felt the crushing weight of his gun barrel on their heads. The third man, who went for his gun while Wyatt still was several paces away, caught a bullet through the flesh of his upper arm, and was taken to the doctor to be patched up, before being lugged off to jail, there to join the other two who had been knocked unconscious.

Rarely, any more, was there the sound of gunfire in Wichita. Men who felt the urge to fight, fought it out with their fists. In such a battle, both men might be beaten up, but at least both remained alive.

Actually, an uneasy peace had settled over the town. It was an uneasy peace because most men knew it couldn't last. There would be another test of Wyatt Earp's authority, and this time, a real test. No inexperienced or half-drunken gunman would be sent against him. Those who resented the new order in Wichita were banding together, and would ride in a body on the town.

That was the rumor that was going around. The Texans, who had come up the trail with their herds of longhorn cattle, had made Wichita the town it was, and they didn't mean to be ordered around by a tin-star Yankee marshal.

Wyatt had heard these rumors, and had taken what precautions he could against the day of the final test. He had persuaded the mayor to buy him a dozen double-barreled shotguns. These, fully loaded, had been placed in various stores up and down the avenue, stores where the proprietor would co-operate and have the shotgun ready for him should he need it. He also, although he didn't seek them, had his own informers, men who hoped for continued law and order and who had friends in the cowboy camp to tell them what was planned.

"They're going to wait a few days longer," one such man told him. "They're still hoping someone will get you, and save them the trouble."

"I already have met a few of those who wanted to get me," Wyatt said grimly.

He glanced up and down the street. It was night. There were a dozen shadowy places from which a hidden gunman might have shot him down. And that might happen, but he thought it unlikely. The man who got him would want to boast about it. It was the way of those who lived by their guns to want to boast about the men they had shot down. In that streak of vanity lay his safety. A man couldn't boast of having shot another from the dark.

Jeff joined him at the next corner and walked on down the street with him. Nearly every evening they met like this, somewhere along the street, and since the town had quieted down considerably, Wyatt offered no objections to such a procedure. Tonight Jeff had news for him.

"I saw two of them, Mr. Earp," the boy said. "I'm sure of it."

"Two of whom?" Wyatt asked.

"Two of the men who killed my father. You said if I ever saw them, to notify the nearest officer of the law. I guess you're the man I should tell."

Wyatt nodded soberly, recalling the four men he had run into on the road to Ellsworth, almost a year before. He asked, "Where are they, Jeff?"

"In Pryor's. That is, they were a few minutes ago."

"We'll go take a look," Wyatt said.

They continued on down the street, but a few steps farther on were confronted by George Peshaur. His face was flushed and he didn't look very steady, but when he saw Wyatt Earp, he braced himself and a sneer curved his lips.

"Hello, you tin-horn marshal," he grated. "Hasn't anyone killed you yet?"

"Not yet," Wyatt said.

"Someone will."

"Maybe," Wyatt shrugged.

"Maybe I will," Peshaur shouted. "Get out of town, Earp. Get out while you can."

"You're drunk, George," Wyatt said quietly. "Go sleep it off."

He walked on then, ignoring the ugly words Peshaur sent after him, but under his breath he said to Jeff, "There's a man I'm going to have to handle some day. I don't know why he hates me, but he does."

"He's one of Thompson's men, isn't he?" Jeff said.

"I suppose you could tag him as one of Thompson's men," Wyatt nodded, "but he does pretty much whatever he wants to do. Thompson's kept his promise to me, not to cause trouble in Wichita. I could back Peshaur into a corner and force such a promise out of him, but it wouldn't mean anything. Now, what about these men you saw enter Pryor's? Which of the four were they?"

"They were the ones who wore beards. They're big men. One has a red face. I think they just reached town. They still were wearing their guns."

"You're sure you recognized them?"

"Mr. Earp, I'll never forget the faces of the four men who stopped us that day," Jeff said stubbornly.

They came to Pryor's. Wyatt noticed Marshal Smith

across the street. He motioned to him to follow them, and with Jeff at his side, entered the building.

Pryor's was crowded. Every table was in use. The room was filled with smoke and the rumbling sound of men's voices. Several of those near the door saw Wyatt come in and fell silent, watching him soberly, but most of the others in the place weren't yet aware of his presence.

"See the two anywhere, Jeff?" Wyatt asked.

"Over near the wall," Jeff answered. "One is looking this way."

Wyatt glanced in the direction Jeff had indicated. A good many of those in the room were bearded, but he had a good memory, himself, for faces, and he instantly spotted the two Jeff had seen and recognized. In his own mind there was no doubt as to their identity.

"Wait here, Jeff," he said under his breath. "I'll have a talk with them."

He walked toward the two bearded men who stood against the wall. The one who had been staring at him now was looking in the other direction, but his body seemed tense. He whispered something to his companion, who sent a quick glance at Wyatt, then stepped away a yard or two.

Wyatt moved steadily ahead. He stopped near one of the men, then half turned so he could keep an eye on the other.

"Mister," he said abruptly, "don't I know you, and the fellow who came in here with you?"

The bearded man glanced at him, shook his head. "Not so far as I know."

"I figure you're wrong," Wyatt said. "I met the two of you on the road between Abilene and Ellsworth early last August. There were two other men with you at the time."

The bearded man nearest him again shook his head. "Never been up that way in my life."

"I wouldn't admit it, either, if I were you," Wyatt said. "A cattleman named Crandall was murdered and robbed of fifteen thousand dollars that afternoon."

"Don't know a thing about it," the bearded man said sharply.

"I think you do," Wyatt said. "You're under arrest, both of you."

It had grown very quiet in Pryor's. A good many of those who were present had seen Wyatt Earp in action before. They knew he meant just what he said, and that if necessary he would enforce his order with his guns. Such men stepped back out of the line of fire. Others, who hadn't seen the new deputy make an arrest, had heard stories about him, and stood watching curiously.

"You can't arrest us in Wichita for something you say happened on the Abilene road," one of the bearded men protested. "There ain't no law—"

"You can argue that point with the judge," Wyatt said quietly. "Unbuckle your gun belts and drop them. You shouldn't be wearing gun belts in Wichita, anyhow. It isn't the custom any more."

Somewhere in the room a man laughed, but others scowled at that remark. Being deprived of the right and privilege of wearing guns still didn't go well with most Texans.

"I still say you can't arrest us," the man nearest Wyatt declared. "I still say—"

He clawed for his gun, twisting his body sideways. And at the same time, the other bearded man dropped into a crouch and grabbed his Colt.

Wyatt's arms moved with a blinding speed, too swift for the eye to follow. Not since his appointment as deputy had he been forced to reach for both guns at once. There were some who said he wasn't much good with his left hand. But those watching in Pryor's that night said that his two shots came so close to each other, it was impossible to be sure which gun had been fired first.

There was no question, however, as to where his bullets went. Each of the bearded men grabbed a shoulder. And each went down, one without having cleared his gun from its holster, the other before he could fire.

This was going to add immeasurably to Wyatt's fame, and it was going to bring to a head the organized movement against him. But Wyatt, just then, wasn't concerned about his reputation as a gun handler, or what his enemies were planning. He had been faced with a job to do and he had handled it as well as he could. Neither of the two men he had shot was seriously hurt, each would recover to face the bar of justice. It was that which was important.

Day succeeded day. Herd after herd came up the trail from Texas, and with each herd came more cowboys, ready to celebrate the end of the long drive. They discovered they could shoot off their guns all they wanted to, outside of Wichita, but that in the town gun-toting was not allowed.

They didn't like it. It had been their custom to shoot up a town, and to stalk the streets as though they owned it.

Some tried it, in spite of stern warnings. They found that they ended up in jail, and next morning were separated from part of their money by a stony-faced judge. This was a blow to their pride, and a challenge to their manhood. Their resentment grew and festered. Some, who might have ridden on, remained, for there was talk that one day soon the Texans would march on Wichita and make it their own.

The day they did that was a day to look forward to, and would be a day to be remembered.

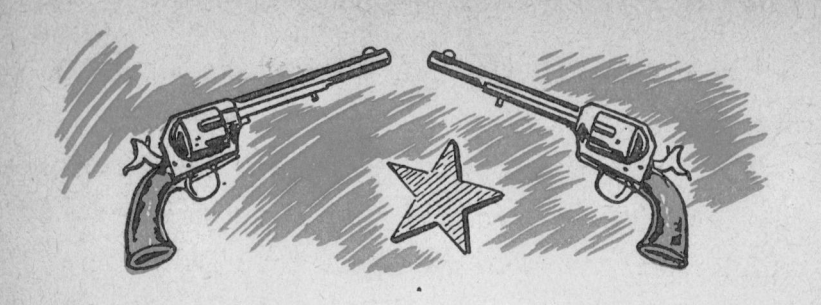

8 • THE DESPERATE HOURS

Mayor Hope was worried. This morning he had had another warning to get rid of his new deputy, Wyatt Earp. He had been warned to do this before, and had ignored such warnings as he would ignore this one. But the latest warning had been more definite than those which had preceded it. A time limit had been included. He had been given twenty-four hours in which to act.

What would happen at the end of that time if he failed to discharge Wyatt Earp, he had been told in blunt, hard detail. The men who had come to see him had put it this way: "Fire Earp, or we'll march on the town and take it over, and when we get through, if there's a pane of glass left in a window anywhere, you'll be lucky. We may even burn the place down."

"Who are *we?*" he had asked.

"By *we*," the man answered, "I mean every Texan who has come up the trail."

This wasn't true, of course. There were many Texans who believed in law and order, and who welcomed the changes in Wichita. But there were enough die-hard rebels among the cowboys to cause a lot of trouble. And a good many younger men would follow their lead, out of love of excitement if for no other reason.

Hope went to see Judge Jewett and repeated the last warning given to him.

"But why are they so dead set against Earp?" Jewett asked. "Other deputies also make arrests."

"It was Earp who gave the other deputies the courage to stand against the Texans," Hope replied. "Wyatt Earp is the backbone of the force, and you know it. Without him, the others would cave in."

"In twenty-four hours," Jewett said scowling. "What do you reckon they'll do in twenty-four hours? March on us like an army?"

"They may, or they may wait longer, make us sweat it out."

"How many men can they count on?"

"A hundred, easily. Perhaps three hundred."

"Three hundred against a handful of deputies. What are you going to do, Mayor? Give in to them?"

"Never," Hope said grimly. "We found in Wyatt Earp exactly the man we wanted. Do you realize what he's done here in Wichita? He's given us law and order without killing a single man. He's made the wearing of guns in town illegal without a statute to back him up. He's done the impossible and done it quietly and without putting on a show. You don't let such a man down."

"But you can't expect him to face an army alone."

"We can revive the citizens' committee."

"He won't stand for it."

"He'll have to. I'll go talk to him."

The mayor found Earp having a late breakfast at the Cloverleaf restaurant. He had been on duty late the night before, and had slept late this morning. In as few words as possible, the mayor told him of the new warning he had received, and of what he had in mind.

Wyatt sipped his coffee. He was silent for a moment, considering what the mayor had proposed, then he shook his head. "I don't want you to revive the committee, Mayor."

"Why not?" Hope asked.

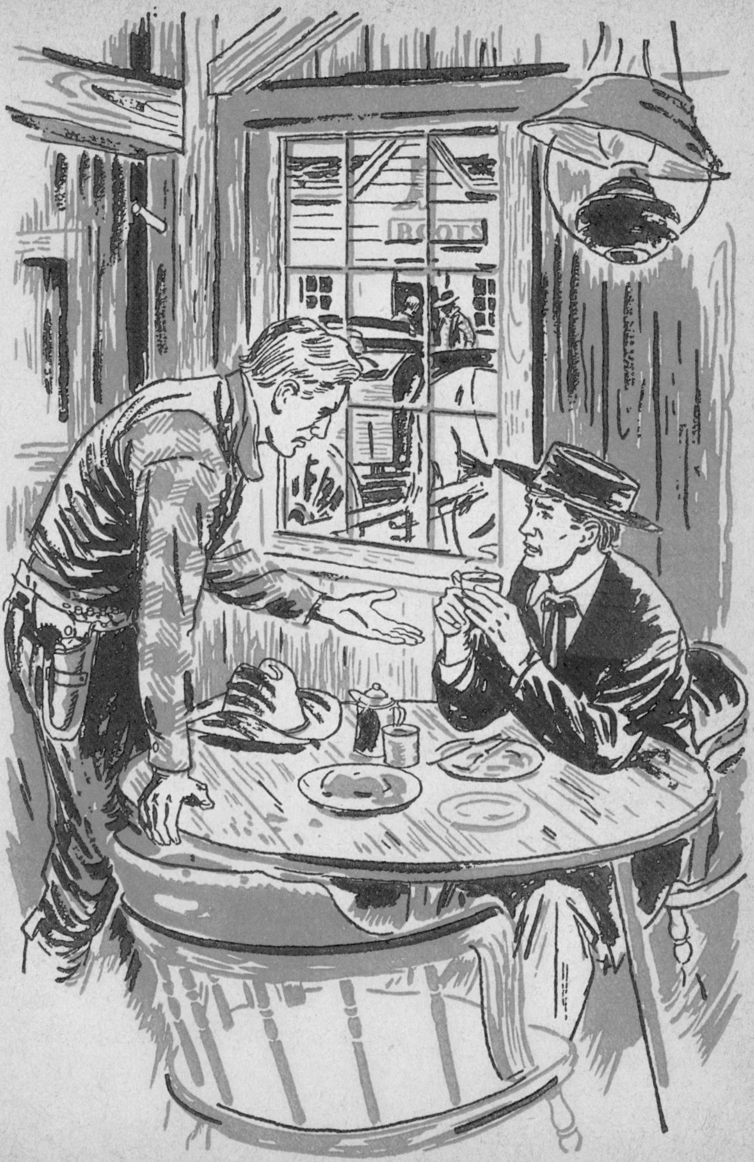
BOOTS

"Let's look at this problem for a minute," Wyatt said. "Suppose three hundred men ride on Wichita. Suppose even a hundred ride this way. And suppose you line up a hundred to face them. What's going to happen when those two hundred armed men bump up against each other?"

"Some will get hurt."

"No, let's be realistic. Some will get killed. In a pitched battle, maybe a good many would get killed."

"But how can you avoid a battle?"

"I don't know," Wyatt said. "Let me think about it for a while."

"We don't have much time."

"Time enough," Wyatt answered.

He finished his coffee, ordered another cup, and sat there at the table after the mayor left. He already had done a good deal of thinking about what he would do when the Texans marched on Wichita, for he had heard rumors of the impending march, long ago. He had made and discarded half a dozen plans intended to avoid serious trouble. He was afraid an out-and-out fight might be inevitable, but if it was at all possible, he meant to find some other solution.

When he had gone to work as deputy he had insisted

that the citizens' committee be disbanded. It then had been composed of a number of men who lived here in Wichita, and who assembled with their guns at the sound of an alarm on a triangle set up in front of Judge Jewett's court. It had been used once or twice to quell riots, and had been used effectively, but the committee was composed largely of men who had had little experience in the use of guns. To stack the citizens' committee against the Texans who might be riding this way would be like sending out raw recruits to stop the march of a well-trained army.

No. The citizens' committee wasn't the answer to the threat against the peace of Wichita. Some other measure must be found.

Jeff entered the restaurant, joined him at his table, and ordered coffee.

"Why aren't you working today?" Wyatt asked bluntly.

"Needed a day off," Jeff said. "Now and then a man needs a day off."

"It couldn't be you took the day off because of a rumor you heard, could it?"

Jeff shrugged. "Who listens to rumors?"

But a flush of color showed in his face and Wyatt knew Jeff had heard of the proposed march on Wichita, and for that reason had left his job to come into town. The boy's loyalty pleased him. Boy? No. Jeff was growing up. He handled a man's job at the cattle pens, and he thought like a man. He would rather have had Jeff at his side in a tough spot than a good many people he could think of who were two or three times Jeff's age.

"Jeff," he said suddenly, "in an emergency, could I count on you to do what I said—and exactly what I said?"

"You bet you could, Mr. Earp," Jeff said, his eyes brightening.

"It's about time you started calling me by my first name," Wyatt said. "Let's forget this mister stuff."

"If you want me to."

"I do, Jeff."

"All right, Wyatt."

Wyatt Earp chuckled, then grew serious. Jeff's sudden appearance here in the restaurant had given him an idea that might be worth while. How many men were there here in Wichita who had the same degree of loyalty, and on whom he could count as safely as he could count on Jeff Crandall?

He began to make up a list in his mind. There were the other deputies with whom he worked and whose loyalty and courage had been tested. There was his brother, Jim Earp, and the mayor, and a man named Simons who worked here in town. There might be a dozen others as dependable.

He got to his feet, smiling. "Let's take a walk through town, Jeff," he suggested. "There are a few men here and there I want to talk to."

Out at the cowboy camp on the creek, Mannen Clements laid his plans for the attack on Wichita. Up to a few days before, he had had John Wesley Hardin to consult with, but Hardin had unexpectedly left them.

A gunman's sudden urge to move somewhere else was quite normal. Hardin might have had a good many irons in the fire, and his presence elsewhere might have been badly needed; yet Clements couldn't help but wonder if the identity of the man they were going to march against had anything to do with Hardin's departure. He suggested this to his brother Gyp.

"I wouldn't say that to Hardin," Gyp advised. "Ain't no one he's afraid of."

"Maybe so," Mannen agreed. "But some pretty brave men have caved in when they faced Wyatt Earp. And it may be they had reason to. I was in Pryor's the other night when he shot it out with the Sanderson brothers. He's as fast with his left hand as his right, and his bullets go where he aims them. The Sandersons were pretty fair gun handlers, as I remember, but they were slow as kids compared to Earp."

"Earp was lucky that night," Gyp scoffed.

"I suppose you wouldn't be afraid to face him."

"No more than you," Gyp said shrewdly.

Mannen rubbed his hands together. He looked into the fire, his expression thoughtful. It was when he had seen Wyatt Earp handle the two bearded Sanderson brothers, that he had decided their policy of waiting for someone to come along and handle Earp just wasn't going to work. The average gunman didn't have the ghost of a chance against the new deputy.

A few of the top men he knew might have been as good with their guns as Earp. But where were they? Ben Thompson sulked in Wichita and would have nothing to do with them. John Wesley Hardin had ridden away. That left him at the head of the list, a position he didn't relish.

"Couldn't be you're afraid of him, yourself, could it?" Gyp asked.

"Shut up," Mannen growled. "We haven't only got Earp to worry about. The other deputies have been getting bad as he is. I want you to go into Wichita and get Peshaur, John Good, Neil Kane, and any other gun handlers you can find. Tell them this. *The time has come.*"

By dusk that evening, Wyatt had picked about a dozen men he thought he could trust, and had talked to each one. He had made a very careful selection. The men he had chosen were men of good and proven judgment. They weren't the type to panic, whatever happened.

He called these men his Number One Posse. They would serve as Wichita's first line of defense.

But he also had chosen a Number Two Posse. Those in the second posse, who also had been carefully selected, would keep the main streets clear when the trouble broke and would see to it that some irate citizen didn't take advantage of the situation, and throw a vengeful shot at the Texans as soon as they rode into sight.

"In a way, your second posse is as important as the first, isn't it?" Jeff suggested early that evening.

"In a way, it's more important," Wyatt answered. "If someone here in town gets excited and starts shooting, the cowboys will shoot back. And if that happens, we may have a battle on our hands."

"Don't we anyhow?"

"Not yet," Wyatt said. "Just because a crowd of men may be riding this way doesn't mean they'll try to shoot their way into town."

"You think they'll turn back?"

"Could be."

"I don't get it," Jeff said, puzzled.

"That's because the problem we face looks so terribly desperate," Wyatt said. "Forget the problem for a minute and put yourself in the other fellow's shoes. Do you think any man riding here wants to get killed?"

"Of course not."

"All right. Now suppose you're one of the men riding this way. You get here and you find yourself facing a crowd which isn't afraid of you. You can move on, but maybe you'll get killed. When a man faces that possibility, and faces it honestly, he usually thinks a second time. What do you suppose makes a successful gunman?"

"Speed in drawing his gun, and shooting straight."

"Both important," Wyatt nodded. "What else?"

"Nerve."

"Surely. But what else, would you say?"

"I don't know, Wyatt."

"Fear," Wyatt said. "The fear that his name builds up in the minds of other men. You're just a youngster. Someday you may have to face a man who has killed half a dozen others in gun battles. You remember that as you stand in front of him, and it terrifies you. You don't want to die. You don't want to be the next on his list. Maybe you back down, or maybe you grab desperately for your gun, and because your fear already has whipped you, you are too slow."

"But don't gunmen know fear?"

"That's just the point. Give any man the time to think about death, and he fears it. Outbluff him, Jeff, but if he doesn't back down, be ready to match your ability against his."

"It isn't bluffing if you're ready to fight."

"But the process is the same. Here's the rule to follow. Stand up to the job you've got to do as though you were equal to it, and ninety-nine times out of a hundred, you'll find you are."

Jimmy Cairns joined them. He said, "Gyp Clements was in town about an hour ago. When he left he took George

Peshaur with him. Kane and Good and six or seven others rode with them."

"Toward the creek?" Wyatt asked.

"That would be my guess. Do you think they'll hit us tonight?"

"Who knows?" Wyatt shrugged.

He had men posted across the toll bridge, watching for the approach of Clements's crowd. He figured that at the worst he would have at least half an hour's warning that they were on their way. But it was a dark night, and that had him worried. He hoped Mannen Clements would hit Wichita in the daylight hours, when a man could see what he was doing.

The evening hours passed slowly. There was less trouble than usual in town that night, but in every place where Wyatt stopped there was an air of expectancy. He could understand it. What the cowboys planned was generally known. For a long time it had been only a rumor, but it was a rumor no longer. Everyone in Wichita knew that the next few hours were critical. The forces standing for law and order were to be challenged.

In Pryor's, a gambler posted a bet, two to one that Wyatt

Earp would be dead before another day had passed, and five to one that the Texans, under the leadership of Mannen Clements, would take over control of the town.

There was no one who would bet against him.

9 • THE SHOWDOWN

Mannen Clements was a shrewd leader. He had a faint hope that some of the men backing Wyatt Earp would drop out of the picture before he and his men reached town. But he couldn't count on that, and of one thing he could be almost positive. Earp wouldn't back down. If the Texans were to take charge of the town, they first were going to have to deal with the new deputy, and with whoever supported him.

With this in mind, Clements decided to start his march on Wichita just before dawn, and to cross over the toll bridge as it was growing light. The dawn hour should find most of the town's residents asleep, and the cowboys should run into less opposition than at any other time in the day. They might even take the place by surprise.

He announced his plans, and picked the men who were

to ride with him. He didn't choose everyone at the camp. He picked men on the basis of their ability to handle their guns, men whom he felt would be willing to take a risk, and who, if it came to an out-and-out fight, could give a good account of themselves. There were about forty who fell into this classification. Forty hard-riding, gun-toting men, who had come up the trail from Texas, and who would sooner fight than eat.

A man left the cowboy camp shortly after he made his plans known, but Mannen wasn't aware of it. If he had been, the chances are he wouldn't have worried about it. It never would have occurred to him that all Texans didn't want what he wanted—a free hand to act as they pleased, in town or out.

The man who carried word to Wyatt Earp of what the Texans were planning didn't look on himself as a traitor. He was as much a Texan as any man in the cowboy camp. He had fought for the South during the war and was bitter over the defeat the Confederacy had suffered. He didn't like Yankees. But he was old enough and wise enough to appreciate the values of law and order. He considered Mannen Clements's plan to be reckless and unwise, something that would hurt the cattle trade more than it would help it.

Wyatt showed no signs of excitement at the report which was brought him. He thanked the man for his warning, then sent Jeff to find Jimmy Cairns.

"Start clearing the west end of Douglas Avenue," he ordered. "I want all the horses off the street, as far down as here. And I want all the places up that way to be closed down. There's plenty of time to do it quietly, and with no fuss."

"I'll pass out the word," Cairns nodded.

"And tell the mayor our Number Two posse is to blanket that end of town. By the time the Texans get here, I want no one on the streets and no one at the windows. Our own men are to keep under cover. Their orders are not to fire until I fire, no matter what happens."

"I'll see the mayor right away," Cairns said.

Wyatt nodded. He said, "Jeff, get someone to help you, and assemble some stuff at the west end of the avenue that can be used to set up a barricade. A low barricade. I don't want any wagons. I want nothing over three feet high. Your best bet is to locate some packing cases that easily can be moved into position."

"I know where I can get packing cases," Jeff said.

"Then hop to it," Wyatt said. "And don't look so solemn. This is just another police problem, Jeff. Get a grin on your face."

Jeff was too excited to grin. He had a feeling that this would be a momentous night. By the chance of his friendship with Wyatt Earp, he was going to have a part in whatever happened. Such a thing was enough to make a man look serious. He couldn't understand why Wyatt wasn't more excited.

Actually, Wyatt was. His stomach was kicking up. His nerves were stretched tight. He didn't know what might happen when Mannen's crowd got here. He was afraid there might be an open battle, and that a number of people might be killed. Such a prospect was a terrible thing to have to live with for the next few hours, but he could see nothing to do but face the Texans when they got here. If he backed down, and Mannen's crowd rode in and took over, all he had accomplished would be lost, and the fight he had made for law and order would have to be made again.

He continued his patrol of the town as though nothing unusual was in the air. While he was in the process of doing this, a worried Mayor Hope found him.

"I just talked to a man from the cowboy camp," Hope told him. "We'd better call up more men."

"Why?" Wyatt asked.

"Do you realize who's riding with Mannen? He'll have his three brothers, all good gunmen. Peshaur, Kane, and Good. The Dixon boys. Arch Samuels and Billy Weintraub and Lou Evans. That's only naming a few, all tough."

Wyatt shook his head. "If we get more men, someone is sure to get excited and cut loose with his gun. If that happens, we'll have a war on our hands. The men I've picked aren't the kind to get excited."

"Don't we already have a war on our hands?" Hope cried.

"Maybe. But no one's been hurt, so far."

"You think you can stop the men riding here—without firing a shot?"

"I can try it, Mayor. I've got to try it."

"You're out of your mind."

Wyatt managed a grin. He said, "Mayor, did you promise me co-operation when you hired me as a deputy?"

"Of course I did, but—"

"Then co-operate."

The mayor mopped his face with one hand. He wondered how in the world Wyatt Earp could hope to stop Mannen Clements's crowd without the use of guns. Then it came to him that Wyatt had done a good many things since his appointment as deputy which had seemed impossible. Perhaps he might even do this.

Wyatt moved on down the street. He arrested two men who had started a fight in Longstreet's and were in the process of breaking up the furniture. He arrested another man who had failed to check his gun and whose temper was getting ugly enough to make him dangerous. It was toward dawn, and while he was locking this man up in the jail, that Jeff found him.

"They're coming," Jeff reported tensely. "They've been seen crossing the flats toward the river."

"Then I reckon we'd better go up to the end of Douglas Avenue and be sure our welcoming committee is ready," Wyatt said. "Did you get the packing crates for the barricade?"

Jeff nodded.

"Is the street clear?"

"It's clear halfway through town."

"Are our men there?"

"Everyone you picked."

"Come on, then," Wyatt said. "Let's get this settled before breakfast."

Light had come into the sky. The night shadows still clung close to the buildings along Douglas Avenue, but they were thinning and soon would be gone. It was an apparently deserted street as Jeff and Wyatt moved along it toward the west edge of the city, but here and there indistinct figures could be seen at the corners of buildings.

"Good luck, Wyatt," a gruff voice called.

"We're back of you, Wyatt," whispered someone else.

"Just say the word, and I'll be out in the street, shooting," another man offered.

Wyatt waved each time a man spoke. Their voices, and what they said, encouraged him. He was pretty sure Mannen Clements didn't have any idea how much Wichita had changed. The Texan didn't appreciate that the men who lived here, having had a taste of law and order, meant to keep them. A few weeks ago the cowboys would have had a much better chance of taking the town than they did this morning.

He came to the end of the street and stared ahead at the

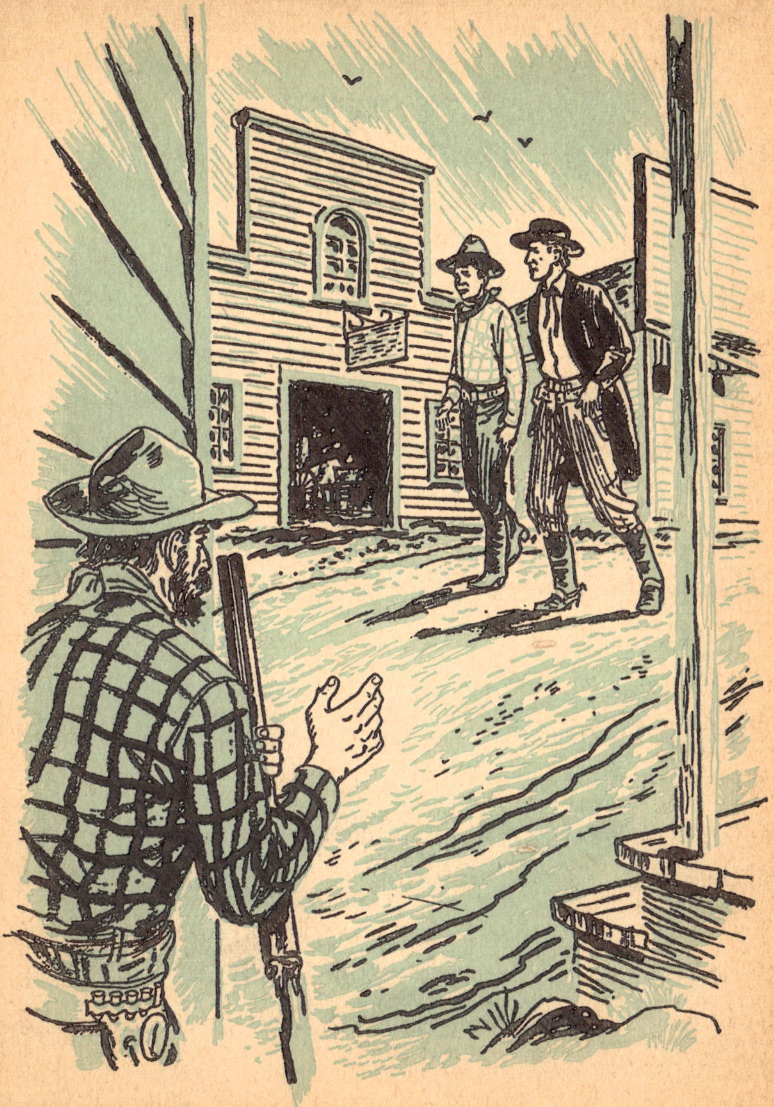

toll bridge. Clements's crowd still wasn't in sight. To one side were the packing cases Jeff had assembled, and gathering around, now, were the dozen men he had picked to make the first stand against the Texans.

"They'll be crossing the bridge in another few minutes," Cairns said. "The guard we had posted at the other end just rode in to say they were only a mile or two away."

Wyatt nodded. "Stretch the packing cases across the street, end to end. Spread out behind them, but stand up, where you can be seen. And hold your rifles ready."

The packing cases were quickly moved into the street. The men in his Number One posse took positions behind them.

The sky was brighter now. Wyatt looked down the deserted street, then glanced at the men stretched across it, back of the packing cases. This was what Mannen Clements's crowd would see after they crossed the toll bridge. A barricaded street, and a reception committee of riflemen. Such a sight would tell Mannen two things. That his march on the town had been expected, and that any attempt to enter the town would be opposed.

"They're crossing the bridge," someone called.

Wyatt already had heard the sound of hoofbeats on the

planks of the bridge. He moved a little ahead of the barricade and stood against a post, watching. Led by the two Clements brothers, the Texans were approaching Wichita. They fanned out a little when over the bridge, but kept coming forward. Then at a signal from Mannen Clements, they reined up.

Clements had seen the reception committee!

Wyatt remained where he was. It was steadily growing brighter, but he doubted if it yet was light enough so that Clements or anyone with him could identify the members of the reception committee.

The sound of a mumbled order reached him, and as he stood watching he saw the Texans dismount. Some, who apparently had been chosen to hold the horses, gathered up the reins. The others crowded around Mannen Clements, possibly for instructions.

Wyatt pushed back his hat. He made sure his guns were free in their holsters. He was frowning. He didn't like the way things were shaping up. It looked as though the cowboys weren't going to be frightened off by his welcoming committee. Dismounted, the Texans could take a steady and sure aim at the men they could see in the street.

But they weren't going to do that yet. Mannen broke out

of the crowd around him and started forward. The others followed, some carrying rifles, some with drawn Colt .45's in their hands.

Wyatt straightened. He called out his last order to the men in the street.

"No matter what happens, don't anyone shoot until I do. Hold steady, right where you are."

He moved into the street then, where he easily could be seen. He started across it, stopped in the middle, and turned to face the Texans. He hadn't drawn his guns but his hands hung at his sides, brushing the gun butts. And every man in the crowd facing him knew how swiftly he could whip those guns into the air, and how accurately he could fire them.

Mannen was quite close to him now, scarcely ten steps away. He had stopped there, and his crowd had stopped behind him. Mannen knew, and those with him knew, that this man who had walked out to meet them was the enemy, the one who stood in the way of their control of the town, the stumbling block in their path. Those behind him might cause them trouble, but it was Wyatt Earp who had put teeth into the law in Wichita, and who had stiffened the other deputies into following his example.

It was Wyatt who spoke first. "That's far enough, Mannen. You've come far enough."

"We're coming on into town!" Mannen shouted.

Wyatt shook his head. "No, you're not. You fellows from the creek can ride in peaceful, any time you want to, but you can't ride in at this time in the morning, armed to the teeth and looking for trouble."

Mannen took a step forward. "I said we were coming ahead."

"But you're not," Wyatt snapped. "Put up your guns, Mannen. Turn around and lead your crowd back to the creek."

He was leaning slightly forward. His arms were no longer swinging at his sides. They were lifted a little, his hands poised over his guns. And in the tense moment which followed, Mannen Clements learned the lesson that Ben Thompson had learned back in Ellsworth. He could defy this man Wyatt Earp. He could cut loose with his guns. He might even kill the new deputy. But as surely as he did, he would die himself. Even with a bullet in him, Wyatt Earp would get him.

A feeling gripped him which was like nothing he ever before had known. It was a feeling that tied a knot of panic in his stomach, and that brought a clammy perspiration to the surface of his body. It dried up his mouth and made him run short of breath. There was a name for this feeling. It was called Fear.

A shudder ran over his body. He knew, dully, what he was going to do. It was all he could do, all he could make himself do, for he didn't want to die. He turned, on legs that were suddenly rubbery. He walked back toward where the horses were being held.

A man turned to follow him. Three more turned. Then five more, and then the others.

They mounted their horses, rode toward the toll bridge and across it.

Wyatt Earp stood in the middle of the street, watching their retreat. He felt no great exaltation. Instead, he felt tired, terribly tired, almost shaky. He reached up to straighten his hat, then stiffened. From across the bridge he heard the sound of a shot. He listened for another, for some sign that the Texans might be coming back, determined to shoot their way through the town.

But nothing like that happened. The horsemen who had recrossed the bridge didn't turn back. The shot he had heard, an angry shot fired at the town, had fallen short of its mark. It was the only shot fired in what might have been a battle costly to both sides.

Wyatt swung around to walk down Douglas Avenue. He called, "Jeff, take down the barricade. The show's over."

He was right. There would be several other individual attempts to question his authority in Wichita, but the organized movement to overthrow the forces of law and order had failed, and would not be tried again.

10 • THE FINISHING TOUCHES

There was an uneasy calm in Wichita. The reason for this was easy to understand. Men like the Clements brothers, George Peshaur, the Dixons, and those who had ridden with them, didn't accept defeat in good spirit. At least some among them would try to square the score with Wyatt Earp. And so Wichita waited, and watched, and wondered how long it would be until something happened.

Wyatt could feel the increasing pressure of each passing day. He was a marked man, and he knew it. Someone, now, might try a shot at him from the dark, or it wasn't unlikely that a trap would be set up to snare him.

He talked this over with the other deputies, and, following their advice, usually took one of them with him on his patrol duties. Then one day he decided to come to grips with his problem, and sent word to Mannen Clements that he wanted to see him right away.

He didn't know what he was going to run into when he had his talk with Mannen. He knew it might end in a fight, for although the Texan had backed down at the edge of town a few days before, by this time he might have prodded himself to the point of wanting to get even.

"Why did you send for me?" Mannen asked when they met.

"Because most Texans will listen to you," Wyatt answered. "I want you to save yourself, and me, and them, a lot of trouble."

"How?"

"Tell them to behave in Wichita. Tell them to check their guns when they hit town. They can yell all they want to. They can fist fight within reason. But no rough stuff goes. If I have to go on telling them that, I'm going to have to break a few heads. If you tell them, they'll behave."

Mannen was silent for a moment. He finally nodded. "All right, Wyatt, I'll do it. I don't know that they will listen to me, but I'll give it a try."

Wyatt took a long, deep breath. He could feel his muscles starting to relax. This was an easier victory than he had expected. He didn't know exactly why Mannen Clements was falling into line, but he thought that it might have been his appeal to the man's position as leader of the Texans. And he was sure that if Mannen kept his word, half his troubles were over.

This left George Peshaur and the town crowd to be dealt with. Ben Thompson was behaving himself, but Peshaur and half a dozen others still were determined to have things their own way in Wichita. Wyatt had been warned several times to keep an eye on Peshaur, and he did. Peshaur, however, in spite of his bullish talk, was careful not to violate the law and make himself liable to arrest.

Then one night as Wyatt was patrolling Douglas Avenue he heard his name called and he swung around to face a young cowboy who held a gun in each hand.

"I'm going to kill you, Earp," the cowboy shouted. "That's what I'm going to do. I'm going to kill you."

Wyatt stood perfectly motionless. He didn't know the cowboy, although he had seen him earlier in the evening talking to Peshaur.

"Did you hear me, Earp? I'm going to kill you," the cowboy cried again.

"I heard you," Wyatt said quietly.

His arms hung at his sides, his hands close to his

holstered guns. He was alone tonight. Cairns hadn't been feeling well and had taken the evening off. There had seemed to be no reason he shouldn't. Wyatt had run into no trouble like this before.

But he was in trouble, now. Real trouble, unless he was lucky.

The cowboy was enjoying his moment of triumph. He seemed confident of his command of the situation. "Why don't you grab for your guns?" he shouted. "They tell me you're fast. Let's see how fast."

Wyatt still didn't move. He was watching the cowboy quite closely. He saw him relax, supremely confident, and then heard him laugh, and say in a taunting voice, "So you're the great Wyatt Earp. But tonight there's water in your veins, isn't there? Tonight—"

Wyatt's right hand and wrist moved so swiftly, no eye could have followed the motion. His gun whipped out of its holster and exploded the minute the barrel was level.

The cowboy shrieked with pain as a bullet ripped into his shoulder. The force of the shot twisted him sideways. He forgot the guns he was holding. He dropped them, and with his right hand clutched his left arm. Then his knees folded and he sank down on the boardwalk.

Wyatt stepped forward, knelt beside him. He asked, "Son, who put you up to this? You never saw me before. You didn't have any reason to kill me."

The cowboy stared up at him, frightened. "Am I going to die?"

"I don't think so," Wyatt said. "You're not badly hurt. Who sent you after me? Whose idea was it?"

He had to ask several more times before he got the name, but he finally got it, and when he did, he walked straight to the Keno Hotel. Inside, he found George Peshaur. He came straight to the point.

"Peshaur, we don't have room for men like you in Wichita. Pack your stuff and get out of town. You've got exactly one hour."

Peshaur's face turned a beet red. "You've got no right to order me around, Earp."

"Then it's not an order I'm giving you, but it's good, sound advice. Pack your stuff and get out of town within an hour."

"I won't do it," Peshaur shouted. "No one can run me out of town."

"I'll be back in an hour," Wyatt said.

He turned and left the building, and an hour later,

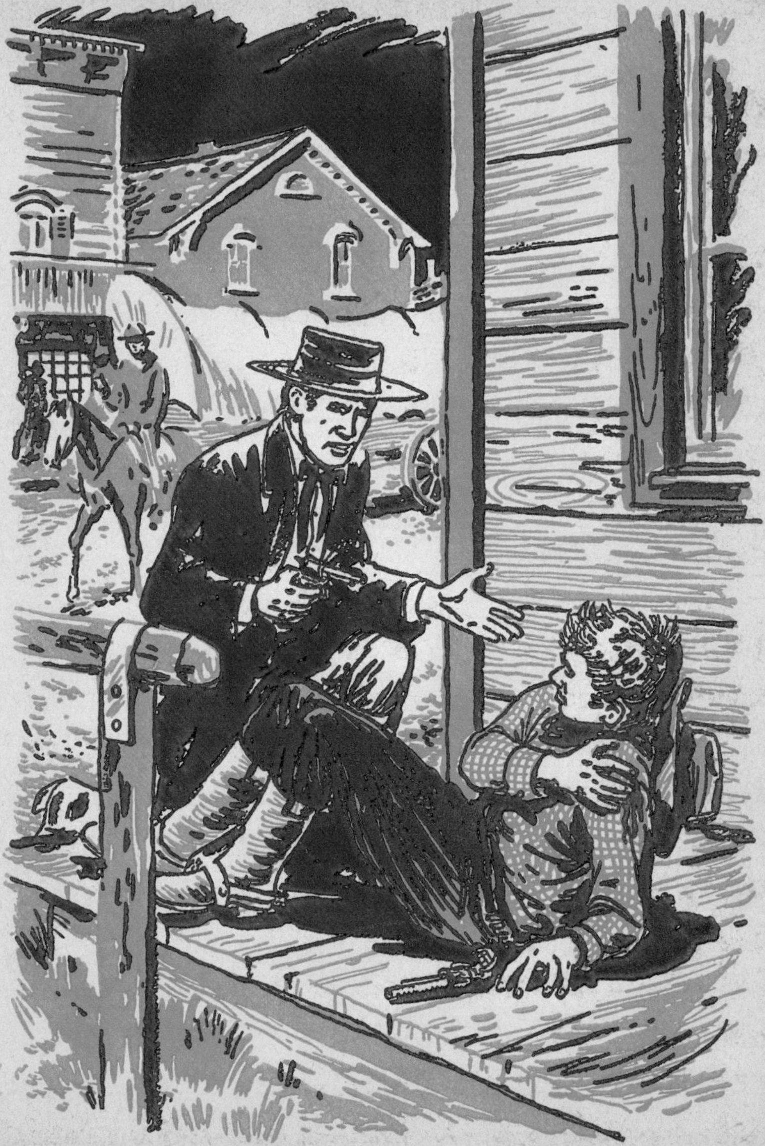

returned. George Peshaur wasn't there, nor was he seen in Wichita again that season.

Things calmed down after that. Mannen Clements, as good as his word, kept the Texas cowboys in line, and Ben Thompson used his influence on Neil Kane, John Good, and the others who still would have liked to see the end of Wyatt Earp's type of law.

In the days that followed, occasionally a cowboy got out of hand and had to be arrested for the night, or someone newly up the trail from Texas resented the order to check his guns while in town, and had to be persuaded that times had changed since a year ago.

The Sanderson brothers recovered sufficiently from their wounds to face Judge Jewett. They denied having had anything to do with the death of Jeff's father, but Wyatt's evidence, with what Jeff had to say, was enough to convict them. From the money in their possession when they were arrested, close to eight thousand dollars were recovered, which the judge ordered turned over to Jeff.

"I could join you in going into the cattle business now," Jeff told Wyatt. "That is, we could go into the cattle business if you ever get tired of working as a marshal."

"Things have been awfully peaceful lately," Wyatt said. "Maybe we'll do something like that, Jeff."

But it wasn't to work out that way. In November, a man from the United States Marshal's office came to Wichita to see Wyatt Earp.

"Ever hear of Frank McMurray?" the government man asked.

"Who hasn't?" Wyatt replied. "Any cowboy who has come up the trail from Texas can tell you about Frank McMurray."

"Especially George Ulrich," the government man said. "Ulrich was driving a herd up the trail. When they were passing through that part of the country which we call the Nations, McMurray's crowd hit them, drove off the crew, and stole the cattle. Seventeen hundred head. Ulrich's an important man in Texas. He complained to the government. We've sent three posses into the Nations after the cattle—and McMurray. They returned empty-handed."

"Why?"

"They said McMurray's crowd was too strong to be attacked. But Ulrich still is complaining. He said to send Earp into the Nations, if we wanted action."

"A Texan said that?" Wyatt asked, grinning.

The government man nodded. "Will you take the assignment, as a Federal marshal? Will you go after those cattle and as many of McMurray's crowd as you can bring out?"

"I'll think about it," Wyatt said.

But he already had made up his mind he would do it. He had been in Wichita now, for more than six months. It was November. The cattle season was over. The population of the town had dropped to nearly normal. Most Texans had gone back down the trail to ready herds for a drive north in the spring. The police problems in town amounted to nothing. But more important, Wyatt felt the trip would be good for him. He felt he needed the exercise of long rides, and the challenge of a new job.

That night he talked to Jeff Crandall about it, telling him what he knew about McMurray, and his partner in crime, Bill Anderson. McMurray was an outlaw, a renegade, the leader of a band of wanted men. He was getting rich through the robbing of those who came up the trail from Texas, and as a sideline he sold whisky and other contraband material to the Indian tribes in the Nations. Bill Anderson had served with Quantrill's guerrillas during the war, and was as violent and evil as McMurray.

"It'll make the cattle trail safer if we take care of McMurray's crowd," Wyatt said. "And it'll be another step forward in establishing law and order in the West. Of course, if we go after McMurray and Anderson, we won't be able to go into the cattle business."

"You mean, I can go with you?" Jeff cried.

"Don't see why not," Wyatt answered. "It's a job I couldn't do alone. I'll need a posse. You're still pretty young, Jeff, but some men grow up long before others. At seventeen I was driving a stage, and I had some rough times while doing it."

"When do we start?"

"In a day or two, I reckon."

Jeff's eyes were sparkling. "Our cattle business can wait," he nodded. "There are lots of years ahead."

They rode south to the Nations, and from the first day out, Wyatt Earp enjoyed this new venture. It was good to feel a horse between his legs again, and to have a night of restful sleep after a long day's ride. It was good to smell the wood smoke of a campfire in the early dusk and to eat the common food men cooked over such a fire. It was good to feel the wind in his face, and to wake up in the half light of the dawn, ready for another day's journey.

This was a different life from life in town. The tensions he had lived under were gone. He didn't have to be constantly on guard against some enemy.

Wyatt had been told that the McMurray-Anderson crowd was holding the stolen herd in the Wewoka valley. From a survey trip he had made through this country five years before, he knew how to reach the valley without following the usual trails. In this way, he hoped to be able to surprise the outlaws, and he did.

Wyatt hit the outlaw camp at dusk. One flurry of shooting, and the battle was over. The outlaws were lined up, disarmed, and then questioned about McMurray and Anderson, who weren't present. Where they were, no one seemed to know.

"What will we do with them?" Jeff asked.

"Set them free, but without their guns," Wyatt ordered. "We came here chiefly to recover Ulrich's cattle. We'll drive them to the next valley and hold them there until spring, then head north."

Jeff felt uneasy as he watched the outlaws ride away. He was afraid they might get guns somewhere and return and cause them trouble.

Some did. A month later, led by McMurray and Bill Anderson, the outlaws made a desperate effort to recover the herd, but the fire of Wyatt's posse was so deadly accurate that they gave up, and fell back, half their number dead or wounded.

McMurray and Anderson made one more attempt to take the herd, and succeeded, but for only a short time. They were not dealing with an ordinary trail crew, and they learned this to their sorrow. Wyatt and his chief deputy cornered them and disarmed them. And when the stolen herd was driven on to Wichita in the spring, McMurray and Anderson went along as prisoners, to be delivered to Federal authorities.

That spring, 1875, Wichita elected Mike Meagher as city marshal, and Meagher's first official action was to appoint Wyatt Earp his chief deputy, giving him full authority for the enforcement of the law.

"We need your services one more year, at least," he insisted. "We showed the world last year that we could keep the peace here in Wichita, but to make the lesson stick, we've got to do it again."

"You may be right at that," Wyatt admitted. He pinned on the badge Meagher gave him, and added ruefully, "It looks as though I'm never going to get to be a cattleman. I didn't want to spend my life as a town marshal."

"Someone had to do it," Meagher said. "There are easy jobs in this world, and there are hard jobs. Those who measure up to it have to take the hard jobs."

The first crews to come up the trail from Texas hit Wichita just as they had a year before, ready to shoot up the town in a wild celebration. They found, as they had been warned they might, a town ordinance forbidding the use of firearms in town. And they ran into a grim-looking chief deputy who enforced the law.

There were a few gun fights, a few tense and anxious moments in Wichita that summer, but the wild and lawless days of the past were over, and as the months rolled on, the character of the town changed. In fact, the character of the entire area around Wichita was changing. Farmers were moving in on the land once devoted wholly to cattle. Fences were going up. The days of the open range were coming to an end. The new businesses now being started in Wichita were chiefly to serve the farmers and the settlers moving in from the East.

Jeff, who had been working on a cattle ranch west of

town, rode in early in December to complain to Wyatt that this was no longer a cattle country.

"You're almost right," Wyatt agreed.

"Where will the longhorns be driven next year?"

"To some town west of here, I suppose. Someplace where there still is room. Dodge, maybe."

Dodge? Jeff remembered Dodge as nothing more than a collection of huts on the banks of the Arkansas River, not far from an Army post. They had sold their buffalo hides in Dodge, two years before.

"We might find the ranch we want around Dodge," he suggested.

Wyatt smiled. "Let's see what the winter brings, or what happens next spring. You have a good job, Jeff. Hang on to it for a while."

The winter was uneventful, and so was the spring. But the spring brought at least one interesting development so far as Wyatt Earp was concerned. It brought him a wire from George Hoover, the first mayor of Dodge.

11 • A NEW JOB

"You're going to Dodge?" Jeff cried. "But why?"

"It seems they need a marshal," Wyatt answered. "Things are quiet enough in Wichita so I can get away."

"But why do they need a marshal in Dodge?"

"You're still thinking of Dodge as it was two years ago," Wyatt said. "The place has grown, and word is that most of the herds coming up from Texas will be heading that way. The first few already have arrived."

"And they don't have a marshal?"

"Not now. They had one, but some of the toughs hanging around town chased him out. I've talked to several men who have been there quite recently. From what they tell me, Dodge is a wilder town than Wichita ever thought of being. There's a law against carrying weapons in town, but no one pays any attention to it. Gun fights are the rule of the day. Every cowboy riding into town rides in shooting off his forty-fives. One man I talked to said there wasn't an unbroken window in any building."

Jeff was frowning. "You don't have to take the job, Wyatt."

"I know I don't."

"You've already shown people what you can do. You showed them at Ellsworth, and here in Wichita."

"I know."

"But you're going anyhow, aren't you?"

Wyatt's usually steely eyes held a twinkle. "Yes, Jeff. I am."

"Why? You don't need the money."

"No, it's not the money," Wyatt said. "It's just this. There's a job to be done in Dodge, and I can do it. I'm beginning to feel I was cut out for this kind of work."

"You mean you're going to be a marshal the rest of your life?"

"Not that long, but as long as I'm needed. And at whatever place I'm needed. Right now, I'm not needed in Wichita, but I am in Dodge, so I'm going to Dodge."

"You'll run into some of the same men there you ran into here, won't you?"

"Some of the same men."

"They'll know you, know you mean business when you give an order."

"And that should help," Wyatt said. "But it's not the entire story. You know, I was meant to be a lawyer. I was studying for it when I was younger than you. I've always been a great reader, and lately I've been reading history. Through the ages, whenever men have failed to be vigilant, the lawless have taken over. You never can relax your guard if you want to maintain an orderly civilization. You have to teach the same men the same lesson, over and over."

Jeff nodded. He said, "When are we leaving, Wyatt?"

"We?" Wyatt repeated.

"Sure. We're going into the cattle business together, sometime, aren't we? And besides that, Wichita's no longer a good place for a cattleman."

Wyatt was pleased that Jeff wanted to go with him. He had grown accustomed to his close association with the boy. He would have missed him a great deal if Jeff had stayed here in Wichita.

"I suppose we'll be leaving toward the end of the week," he suggested.

"Fine," Jeff said. "I'll be ready by then."

Dodge always had been a rough and lawless town. It lay on the mud flats of the Arkansas River, within the shadow of an Army post. In its earliest days it had been a place for soldiers to go when off duty, a place where they could celebrate whatever they wanted to, without Army interference. It later had been a supply point for the buffalo trade, and a center where hunters could market their hides.

Now the cattle trade was moving in on Dodge. The land around Wichita, chopped up by farms, didn't leave enough free acreage to graze the longhorns until they could be sold and shipped east. But around Dodge was all the free land the cattlemen needed.

Within sight of the town, Wyatt and Jeff reined up. From a distance, Dodge looked like Ellsworth in its early days, or like Wichita. Around the more or less permanent frame buildings were shacks, tents, sod huts, and along the railroad were acres of cattle pens.

"Another boom town," Jeff said.

"That's right," Wyatt nodded. "And it will pass through the same stages as Abilene, Ellsworth, and Wichita. It will have its wild days, but will calm down. Farmers will move in and fence this land we're riding through, and the cattleman will disappear. He'll move even farther west."

"We're seeing a state grow up, aren't we?"

"That's a good way to put it."

"What will happen to the cattle drives?"

"They will come to an end. Cattle ranches will be established up here on the land not taken up by farmers. Some day soon, Texas cattle will be marketed directly from Texas. We live in changing times."

"But right now, you've got a boom town on your hands."

"I'm afraid so," Wyatt nodded.

They rode on, through the lower end of town and to the railroad. A sign posted there, in the center of the street, read:

> THE CARRYING OF FIREARMS IN DODGE IS STRICTLY PROHIBITED. CHECK YOUR GUNS AT THE FIRST PLACE YOU STOP.

The sign was shot full of holes. Three men standing on the corner were armed.

"It's a good law, anyhow," Wyatt murmured.

They rode on, dismounted in front of a place called the Long Branch, went inside, and asked for George Hoover.

"You'll most likely find him at the barbershop," some man answered. "Hey, isn't your name Earp?"

"That's right," Wyatt said.

It had been noisy in the Long Branch when they came in, but at the mention of Earp's name, a blanket of silence stretched through the room. Men playing cards at the tables turned in their chairs to stare. A tall, redheaded man got to his feet and came forward. He was wearing two guns, was blue-eyed, and had a pock-marked face. A scowling face.

"Earp, we heard you had been asked to come to Dodge," he said sharply. "It was a mistake. We don't want you here."

"You mean *you* don't, Dugan," Earp answered.

"Me an' quite a few others," Dugan replied.

Wyatt shrugged. "Sorry."

"Sorry!" Dugan shouted explosively. "You listen to me, Earp. Fork your horse and ride back to Wichita—while you can."

"Is that an order?"

"Yes, it's an order."

"Then I'll give one," Earp said quietly. "Shut up, Dugan."

"What!" Dugan shouted. "Why, you—"

He clawed for one of his holstered guns and as he brought

it up, Jeff saw Wyatt pull a trick he had used several times in Wichita. He lunged forward, chopping out sideways with his left arm, knocking the gun out of line. At the same moment, he whipped up one of his Colts with his other hand, and cut a slashing blow at Dugan's head. It stunned the man, dropped him to his knees, and from there he sprawled out, face down on the floor.

Wyatt's eyes raked over the others in the room. Several had started to draw their guns but had changed their minds. Or perhaps they were waiting for another volunteer champion to step forward. None did.

Wyatt looked at the man who lay at his feet. He had met Dugan first three years ago. He knew him to be a braggart and a bully. He was pretty sure Dugan wouldn't have jumped him unless he thought he had the backing of a good-sized crowd. And perhaps he did have the backing of most of the men here, yet no one was doing anything to help him right now.

"After I'm gone, throw some water on Dugan and wake him up," he ordered. "Tell him I'll be back in about an hour wearing a badge, and if I find him here, I'll throw him in jail."

No one made any answer.

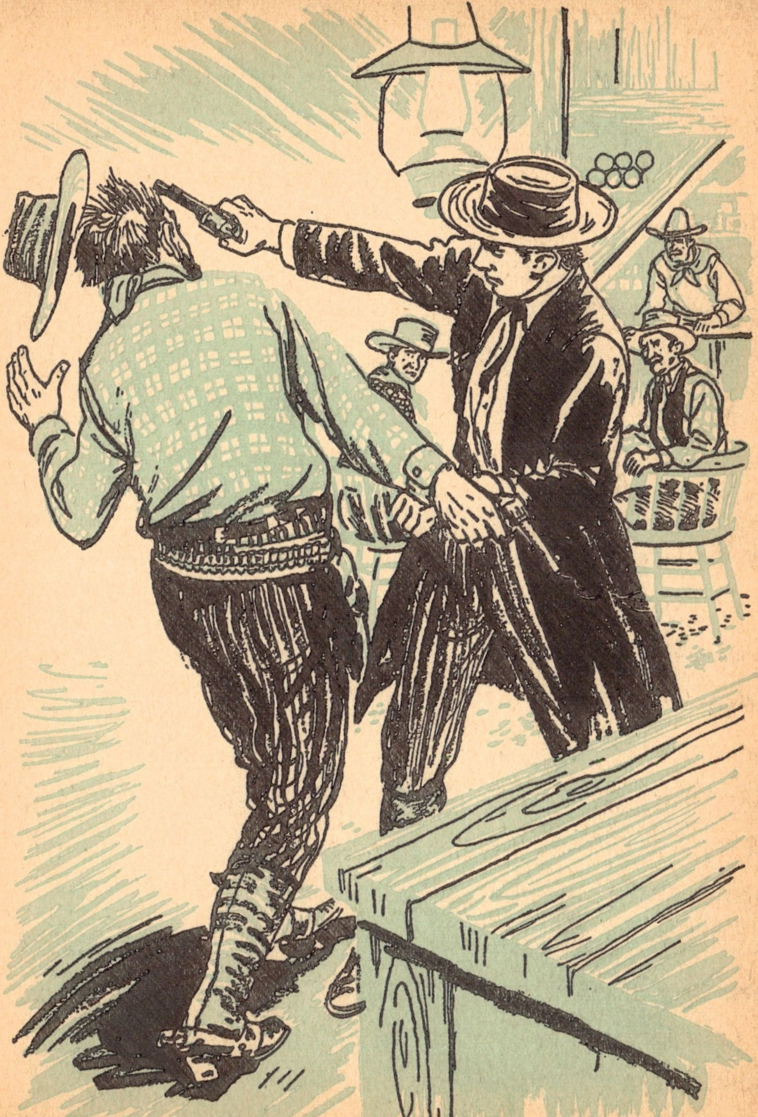

Wyatt turned to the door. Jeff was standing there, his hands on his guns, ready to draw them if necessary.

"Let's go find the mayor, Jeff," Wyatt said.

Jeff nodded and opened the door. He stepped through it. Wyatt followed him, but in the doorway he stopped, turned, and looked back.

"One more thing," he announced clearly. "I saw a sign when I rode into town, forbidding the carrying of firearms in Dodge. Before I get back, the rest of you better check your guns or pull out. The law is the law, and in Dodge, from now on, we're going to live by it."

He still got no answer from any of the men in the Long Branch. He waited for a moment, then stepped out on the walk and, with Jeff, started toward the barbershop, on up the street.

Jeff had felt a sharp excitement there in the Long Branch, when it seemed as though there might be serious trouble. He still was aware of the ragged edge of that feeling. He took a quick glance at Wyatt and asked, "What if they don't check their guns?"

"Then I'll see that they do," Wyatt answered.

"There were thirty men in that room. You can't fight thirty men if they defy you."

"Of course not, but you're forgetting what I told you once before, Jeff. No man wants to die. They know that if they buck me, some will. They could get me, but not before I got a few of them, and every man will be afraid he might be one to go down if there was any shooting."

The barbershop was just ahead. They went inside, asked for George Hoover, and met him. He was awaiting his turn in the barber's chair, but when he heard Earp's name he decided to let his haircut go until another time, and walked with them to his office. There, he pinned a badge on Earp's vest and said with blunt honesty, "I hope you can handle the job, Wyatt. It's not going to be easy."

"Most jobs aren't," Wyatt answered. "Is there really a law on the books prohibiting the carrying of firearms in Dodge?"

"It was passed by the city council, five to four."

"Some councilmen were afraid of it?"

"No. Some didn't think it wise. They didn't want to antagonize the cattlemen with whom they do business. They said it was impractical, couldn't be enforced."

"It'll be enforced," Wyatt said. "Starting today."

The mayor frowned. "You know, I didn't hire you as a killer, Wyatt."

"I'm not a killer," Wyatt said. "I arrest a man who doesn't keep the law. Look at my record."

"I know your record, but this is Dodge."

"And what's so different about Dodge?"

"It's been a wide-open town."

"So was Wichita."

"Do you know Billy Brooks?"

"He used to drive a stage between Wichita and Newton. Yes, I know Billy."

"A tough man. We had him as marshal for a while. The cowboys ran him out of town. Jack Allan was next. They ran him out."

Wyatt smiled. "They won't run me out. Wait here for a few minutes. I'll be back."

He turned to the door and Jeff got to his feet to follow him, but Wyatt shook his head. "No, you wait here, too, Jeff."

Jeff sat down again, looking worried.

"Where has he gone?" the mayor asked after Wyatt left the room.

"To the Long Branch, I think," Jeff answered slowly. "He ran into some trouble there a little while ago with a man named Dugan. He ordered the others in the place to check their guns or get out of town."

The mayor chewed at his lower lip. "I hope he comes back."

"He'll come back," Jeff said.

But he wasn't sure he would. Those men in the Long Branch had been ugly-looking customers.

Wyatt walked directly toward the Long Branch. He wasn't planning anything sensational. He wasn't intending to put on a show, but he meant to see that the order he had given was carried out. He had learned a few things about law enforcement in Ellsworth and in Wichita. He had learned that enforcement had to be rigid and that a man supporting the law had to stand boldly for his beliefs. If the law in Dodge said that men shouldn't wear firearms, then men shouldn't wear firearms. It was as simple as that.

A cowboy standing in front of the Long Branch ducked inside the moment the new marshal appeared on Front Street. Wyatt's lips tightened. It was his guess that the man had been posted there to watch for him, and that could only have been for one reason. The men meant to defy him. He was headed for trouble.

He loosened his Colts, and walked on unhurriedly. He

came to the door of the Long Branch, pushed it open, and stepped inside.

No one there looked around at him as he came in. The men at the tables, playing cards, continued their card playing. Those drinking at the long counter in the room went on drinking. But the place was unusually quiet. The tension which had been built up could have been cut by a knife.

Wyatt moved several steps forward. He looked around for Dugan but didn't see him. Every other man there, however, still was wearing his guns. He had been right in his guess. Dodge meant to defy him.

He swung to the side so that the wall was at his back. He reached out and tapped one of the card players on the shoulder.

"You," he said quietly. "Stand up."

The man looked around at him. He had a thin, deeply tanned face, and pale, gray eyes that were wide with shock. Until now the man probably had been thinking of himself as one of a group, but he was discovering that he had been singled out for special attention.

"Who? Me?" the man gasped.

"Stand up," Wyatt snapped.

The man got to his feet. Perspiration suddenly showed on his face. He took an almost frantic look around the room, searching for the support of anyone who might help him.

"You're still wearing your gun," Wyatt said. "Maybe you weren't here when I said to check it, so I'm telling you again. Walk over to that counter and check your gun."

The man moistened his lips. "I—that is—"

"Now!" Wyatt barked.

He could see the man's courage drain away. He glanced at another man, and said, "You, too. On your feet. Walk over to the counter and check your guns."

"Look here, Earp," someone called from the back of the room. "You can't get away with this."

"I'll get to you later," Wyatt called back. "Or come up here now if you want to argue the matter."

His glance swung from side to side, alert for the motion any man might make to draw his gun. If shooting started, Wyatt wouldn't last long—he knew that. But neither would the man who started the shooting, and no one that afternoon wanted to take the chance of starting a gun duel.

The first man he had ordered to check his gun shuffled to the counter and did so. The second man followed him.

Wyatt motioned to a third, then backed up to the wall and leaned there. Fully half of those in the Long Branch left, still wearing their guns, and rode out of town in preference to yielding to his order. But the others, to a man, checked their guns and then returned in a grim silence to their card games.

Wyatt turned to the door. He had won his first and his second battle in Dodge, but the struggle was far from over. He could sense an ugly undercurrent of anger in the attitude of the men who had left, and those who still remained. Perhaps the mayor had been right in saying that Dodge wouldn't be like Wichita, that Dodge was a tougher nut to crack.

12 • WYATT MEETS A KILLER

Wyatt had been given authority to hire three deputies to work with him. He chose Bat Masterson, his brother Jim Masterson, and a man named Joe Mason. He had been tempted to give in to Jeff's entreaties and make the boy one of the deputies, but his youth still stood in the way.

"You're steady enough for it, I know," Wyatt agreed. "You've learned to handle your guns and you are pretty good with your fists, but there are men who'd pick a fight with you because you're so young, because they'd think they could get away with it."

"So I've got to wait a year or two longer," Jeff said, disappointed.

"That's the way of it."

"But in an emergency—"

"You're the first one I'll call on."

This made Jeff feel better. He set off to look for a job. In Ellsworth and Wichita he had worked at the cattle pens. He figured he might find a similar job here in Dodge, and he did. Such a job was ideal to his purpose. It kept him busy during the day, but gave him his nights off so he could spend them in town, handy to Wyatt if the marshal needed help.

Both Masterson brothers were well-known gun handlers but Bat Masterson probably was the more famous. He at one time had been marshal in Abilene, and recently, in a gun duel in Texas, had killed a man who had been held equal to Ben Thompson and Mannen Clements. Joe Mason had the looks of a stubborn, steady man.

Wyatt had a meeting with his deputies before putting them to work. This was after he had had an opportunity to make a pretty complete survey of the town. There really were two business sections, one below and one above the railroad tracks. The old town, the main part of Dodge, lay north of the tracks. Below the tracks were several cowboy camps and a street called Texas Street. There were a number of card rooms along it, similar to the Long Branch, a few stores, and buildings with rooms to rent.

"We'll do what we can to begin with," Wyatt told his

deputies. "Two towns are too many to handle. We'll draw a deadline along the railroad tracks, and at first we won't worry too much about what happens below the deadline."

"We'll have to clean up there sometime," Bat warned.

"Then we will," Wyatt agreed. "But starting right now, men live by the law once they cross the tracks. Guns are to be checked. There will be no fighting. Anyone who gets out of line goes to jail. And no killing. I want to see men who break the law get arrested. I don't have the time to go to funerals."

"Maybe we shouldn't wear our guns," Jim Masterson drawled.

"You can shoot well enough to hit a man in the arm if you have to," Wyatt answered. "So can your brother. And if Joe Mason can't, he'd better turn in his badge. Killing a man just makes our work harder, for it gives the friends of the man who was killed an excuse to come after us. A wounded man usually gets well—and has learned a lesson."

"Any other orders?" Bat asked.

"Yes. There's to be no drinking on the job. You know me well enough to know how I feel about drinking. I never touch the stuff. You can't drink and last very long at the job we're doing. Steady nerves don't come out of a bottle."

In the days that followed, Dodge learned that the new marshal meant what he said. A crowd, bent on defying the edict against carrying weapons, left their horses on Texas Street, crossed the Deadline, and paraded up and down Front Street, shooting off their guns and daring the forces of the law to do anything about it. Curiously, Earp and his deputies were nowhere to be found. Then one in the crowd caught sight of Joe Mason hurrying across the street some distance away.

A shot lifted Mason's hat from his head. Another shot tugged at the shoulder of his coat. More bullets ripped into the ground at his feet. Everyone was ready to join in the fun when the blast of a shotgun fired into the air brought a sudden silence. A moment later, Wyatt's voice cut through that silence.

"Stand where you are, every man-jack of you. The other barrel of this shotgun is loaded. And if that isn't enough, Bat Masterson is behind you with a double-loaded shotgun and his brother Jim is down the street with another."

Some in the crowd looked around and saw Bat Masterson who had stepped from a store doorway, a shotgun leveled at them from his shoulder. Down the street, his brother Jim had moved into sight with another shotgun.

Mason, by this time, had reached the front of a hotel, and from inside the hotel someone put a shotgun in his hands. From four angles, the crowd in the street was covered. Here in Dodge, just as in Wichita, Wyatt Earp had had shotguns hidden at convenient points for just such an occasion as this.

None in the crowd from below the Deadline wanted to risk a fight against the spraying death from four loaded shotguns. They surrendered their arms and were marched to jail.

There, one of them said bitterly, "Just wait until Clay Allison gets here, Earp. He's on his way."

Wyatt shrugged, but made no other answer. He had been told on several previous occasions that Clay Allison was coming to Dodge, that someone had sent for him. Who, he didn't know.

That night Jeff asked him about Clay Allison.

"What have you heard about him?" Wyatt inquired.

"That he's a killer. And that he's on his way to Dodge."

"I've heard the same story," Wyatt admitted.

"Is he as good with his guns as they say he is?"

"He's fast, I suppose. He killed the sheriff in Cimarron, and in Las Animas, and got off on the plea of self-defense.

He's killed several other men—how many, I don't know."

"What will you do when he gets here?"

"If he behaves himself, nothing. If he insists on wearing his gun in town or causes me any trouble, arrest him, just like anyone else."

"But if he's coming here to kill you—"

"What interests me more than that is who sent for him," Wyatt interrupted.

He knew that some of the merchants in Dodge didn't approve of his strict enforcement of the law. A man thrown into jail and fined the next morning didn't have as much money to spend as he had before his fine. And a Texas cattleman, angered at the arrest of his men, might next year take his business somewhere else.

Wyatt had had several arguments with a merchant named Rath who thought the marshal arrested men too freely. Another business man, Joel Simmons, had thrown the same charges at him. A cattleman and local politician, Henry Langer, was still another who disagreed with his policies. There were more, but these three were the most outspoken, and Wyatt knew that the time would come when the issue between them would have to be settled.

That time came sooner than he expected. Three nights

later he arrested a man named Davis, a cowboy who worked on one of the nearby ranches, and, probably because of that, considered himself a privileged character in the town.

Davis and a man named Sloan started a fight in the Dodge House. Knives were drawn, and Sloan had been severely wounded when Wyatt walked in the door. He interfered at once, pulling Davis off of the man he was about to kill.

But that didn't end things. Davis turned on him, slashing at him with his knife, whereupon Wyatt pulled his gun, smashed Davis over the head, took his knife away, and started lugging him to jail.

Davis was the prospective son-in-law of Henry Langer. Wyatt didn't know that, although it probably would have made no difference if he had.

Langer was in town that night. He heard of the fight and the arrest of Davis, and he hurried to the jail, arriving just about the time Wyatt got there with his prisoner. A crowd gathered, sensing something out of the ordinary.

Langer was a big, bullish man, used to having his own way. He was a member of the state legislature, and well known throughout most of Kansas. He was planning to run for Congress in the next election.

"Hey, Earp," he shouted at the marshal. "You can't arrest that man. Davis had a right to defend himself."

"When I got there," Wyatt said, "he was about to kill the man he was fighting."

"That's a lie," Langer screamed.

"Were you there?" Wyatt asked.

"I heard what happened."

"But I saw what happened," Earp said.

He unlocked the jail door and thrust Davis inside, then started to lock the door. A hand fell on his shoulder, jerking him around. It was Langer's hand.

"You're going to listen to me," Langer roared. "Davis goes free or you're finished in Dodge."

"He stays in jail," Wyatt said.

Langer lost his head. He grabbed for the keys still in Wyatt's hand. There was a brief struggle. It ended with Earp's gun crashing down on the politician's head, and with Langer being tossed into the jail with Davis.

An hour later, Wyatt dropped in to see the judge.

"They'll both come up in front of you tomorrow," he said bluntly. "And they've both got to be treated just like any other men who violate the law. If I had made the mistake of listening to Langer and had set Davis free, the law

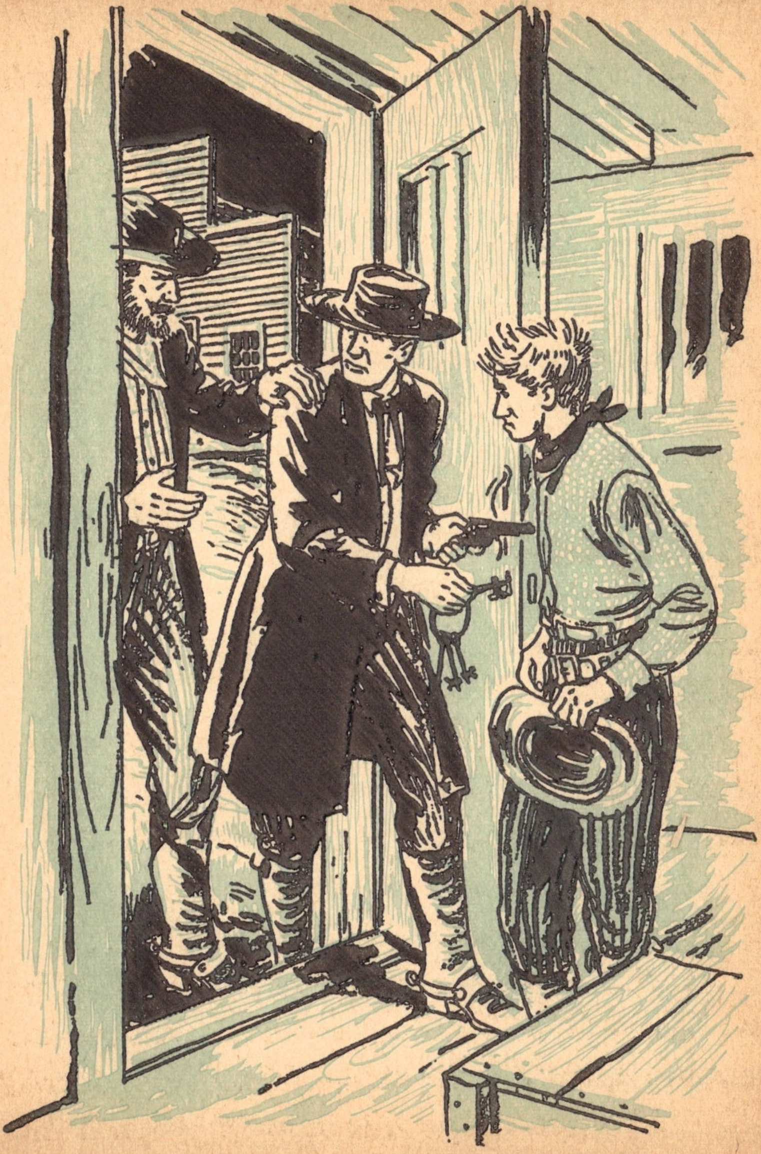

in Dodge would have collapsed. The chief strength of the law is that it applies to all men alike, the rich and the poor, the strong and the weak."

"Langer will kick up an awful fuss about this," the judge warned.

"Let him. He has no defense for what he did. He tried to interfere with an officer making an arrest."

The next morning Davis and Henry Langer faced the judge. Each was fined and set free, and although Langer was quite bitter about it and threatened to complain to the governor, the trial was a great moral victory for Wyatt Earp.

"You haven't heard the last of this, young man," Langer shouted at him as he left the courtroom. "You will regret this business as long as you live—which may not be very long."

The words sounded to Wyatt like another empty threat. He grinned at the angry politician.

Wyatt had fallen into the habit of walking a patrol of the town from about noon until four in the morning, when things finally calmed down. He then would sleep until near noon the next day. For that reason he was somewhat groggy when Jeff Crandall shook him awake one morning at about eight thirty.

Jeff had sobering news.

"Clay Allison's in town," he reported breathlessly. "He's walking up and down Front Street, boasting he'll shoot you on sight."

Wyatt got up, stretched, and started pulling his clothes on. "Has he been drinking, Jeff?"

"Yes."

Wyatt sighed. He said, "Too bad. They say he is a pretty decent fellow when he stays away from the bottle. That's a point to remember."

"What are you going to do?" Jeff demanded.

Wyatt rubbed his jaw. "Why, Jeff, I think I'll finish dressing, then shave, and then have breakfast."

"And after that?"

"After that, one of two things. I'll either have to walk out of here and walk down Front Street, or I'll have to sneak out the back way and leave town."

"That means you're going to meet him."

"I reckon so, Jeff."

"Bat Masterson wants to know if you need any help. Charlie Bassett, too."

Wyatt shook his head. "Tell them I'll be downtown pretty soon. And you might suggest that they cover the street and keep Clay's friends from interfering in whatever happens. You can help in that, too, Jeff. We don't want any open warfare breaking out."

Jeff hurried away, and after he was gone, Wyatt shaved and then had breakfast. He didn't hurry. He knew he would be facing a dangerous man when he went up against Clay Allison, and he knew that the longer Allison had to wait, the more tense and nervous he would grow. Given enough time, the man might work himself up to the point where he could be handled without gunplay. If it came to the point of having to use his gun, he would kill the would-be murderer.

It didn't once enter his head that Allison might be faster than he was with a gun. He had a supreme confidence in his own ability.

It was ten o'clock before Wyatt left his house and started walking. He was wearing both of his guns. He had checked them and settled them loosely in their holsters. He had brushed his boots and the dark pants and coat he was wearing, and had put on a fresh white shirt under his vest. His badge was pinned where it easily could be seen.

The street was almost deserted, but across from the Long Branch he could see Bat Masterson lounging against the wall of a building. Bat was holding one of their emergency shotguns. Farther on was Charlie Bassett with still another shotgun. He was the county sheriff. On his side of the street, near the Long Branch, was Jeff Crandall, and beyond Jeff was Bill Tilghman, a newly appointed deputy. Jeff and Bill were armed with shotguns.

It was easy to guess that Clay Allison was somewhere in the neighborhood of the Long Branch. To make another guess, he was the tall, heavy-set man standing out in front of it.

The horses, usually at the hitching rails along the street, had been moved to points of safety, a sure sign of impending trouble. And such men as were in sight stood close to the buildings, where they could take shelter when the shooting started.

Wyatt moved steadily forward. In spite of his usually calm nerves, he could feel a tightening excitement growing in his body. He knew that what happened in the next few minutes was going to be important to the future of Dodge. Actually, a braggart gun slinger was about to attack the town's marshal, but this was more than a contest between two men. The braggart gun slinger was the champion of the forces who resented the restrictions of the law. The marshal was champion of the law.

He came to where Jeff was standing and heard the boy whisper, "That's him—in front of the Long Branch."

"Thanks, Jeff," Wyatt nodded.

He walked on, came to the corner of the Long Branch, and headed toward the man standing in front of it. Clay Allison now was staring at him, hard-eyed, his hands poised above his holstered guns.

"Are you Wyatt Earp?" he shouted.

"That's my name," Wyatt said. "How come you're wearing your guns? Don't you know there's a law against it in Dodge?"

"I'm going to kill you. I'm Clay Allison."

A twisted smile showed on Wyatt's lips. He stepped closer. "So you're Clay Allison, the famous marshal-killer. And you want to add another notch to your gun. *All right, go ahead. Pull your forty-fives.*"

Allison took a quick, deep breath. His hands shot down to grasp the butts of his guns. He jerked them from their holsters, then froze, with the guns only half lifted. The sharp, hard barrel of a Colt was pressed against his left side just under his heart. Wyatt's thumb was on the hammer.

Allison shook his head in a numb disbelief. It was impossible that anyone could have drawn a gun and shoved it against his side as quickly as Wyatt Earp had done. Yet the gun was there. He was only a few seconds away from eternity. A snap of the gun's hammer, and he would be dead.

The .45's he had drawn slipped from his hands. His shoulders sagged. A gray look came into his face. He started perspiring.

"Where's your horse?" Wyatt asked.

"Down—down the street," Allison mumbled.

"Walk that way, climb your horse, ride out of town. And don't come back."

"You mean—"

"Get started, Allison."

The killer turned away, a thoroughly beaten man. He slouched down the street toward his horse, men watching from every window. He pulled himself into the saddle and headed toward the Arkansas River bridge.

Some, who had watched what had happened in front of the Long Branch, hardly could believe what they had seen.

Yet the facts were there. One of the most famous killers in the West had faced Wyatt Earp and had gone for his guns, but had been covered before he could draw them. And like a whipped cur, he had crawled out of town. Who could the lawless get now who would stand up to the marshal of Dodge? Where would they turn?

13 • A PRICE ON HIS HEAD

"Things ought to quiet down, now," Jeff said that evening as he and Wyatt were having supper.

"I hope you're right," Wyatt nodded. "But some men take a lot of convincing."

He was thinking of some of the Texas cattlemen who had camped below the Deadline and who resented having their crews arrested if they crossed the tracks into Dodge and got into trouble. He also was remembering men like Henry Langer, Joel Simmons, and Pete Rath, who thought their business would be better if law enforcement was not so strict.

"Who persuaded Clay Allison to come here?" Jeff asked.

"I'm not sure," Wyatt said. "It could be that he came on his own. If anyone paid him to come, they threw their money away. Have you finished eating?"

Jeff pushed back his chair, got to his feet, and they went outside. It was dark, but the lamp light shining through the windows and open doors of the establishments along Front Street did much to thin the shadows. It still was warm. This was going to be a hot and sweaty summer.

As they stood on the boardwalk talking, Jeff saw someone step around the corner of a building on down the street, stop, and then suddenly claw at his holster. He shouted a warning at Wyatt and, lunging against him, pushed him into the street. A bullet whistled above the boy's head as he sprawled to his knees. The shadowy gunman ducked quickly out of sight around the corner of the building.

Wyatt scrambled to his feet. He shouted, "Thanks, Jeff," and then started running toward the place from which the shot had been fired. Jeff followed him.

They rounded the building, stopped in the shadows behind it. Jeff could see nothing moving. He strained his ears but couldn't hear the sound of anyone running away.

"He's dived in a hole somewhere," Wyatt growled. "I wonder who it was."

"I couldn't see him clearly," Jeff said. "He was tall and thin, but lots of men are tall and thin."

"Some cowboy out to make a name for himself, maybe."

They walked back to the street. Jeff went home, and Wyatt took up his patrol. He made three arrests that night, and had one rough, touch-and-go encounter with a crowd that crossed the Deadline wearing their guns, determined to shoot up Front Street. But through all this he kept wondering about the man who had taken a pot shot at him from the darkness.

The next evening, three shots were aimed at him from the corner of a cattle car near the station. He raced that way, zigzagging his steps, but by the time he got there the man had fled.

The next night when he entered his hotel room, someone fired a shotgun through the window, but it was a hasty shot, unaimed, and the spraying lead pellets didn't reach him.

Wyatt swung himself through the window and took out after the man who had fired the shotgun. He brought him down with a bullet through the leg, ran to where the man had fallen, and stood above him, menacing him with his gun.

"I want to know just one thing," Wyatt said grimly. "Who hired you?"

The man who lay wounded on the ground was a Texas

cowboy who had reached Dodge with a trail herd only a few days previous. Wyatt couldn't even remember having seen him before. He couldn't guess what the man had against him.

"Who hired you?" he asked again. "Why did you try to kill me?"

"It was—for the thousand dollars," the cowboy gasped.

"What thousand dollars?"

"The thousand dollars they've offered to any man who brings you down."

"Who are *they*? Who is putting up the money?"

The cowboy shook his head. "I don't know—but everyone knows about it. I—I need the money. If I don't raise some money—"

"You're lucky to be living," Wyatt growled.

He turned away to summon help for the man he had wounded, and to give a little serious thought to the problem now facing him. What the cowboy had said explained the two previous attempts on his life, and promised a good many more. A thousand dollars was quite a chunk of money.

Wyatt started asking questions. Who was it who had placed the price of a thousand dollars on his head? Word of the offer spread throughout the town, and across the Deadline to the cowboy camps. Then a strange thing happened. Henry Langer stopped him on the street the next day, and made a statement in the hearing of several others.

"Earp, we've had trouble," Langer said. "I don't like your methods, but I want you to know this. I've had nothing to do with any reward offered to the man who gets you."

That night, two Texas cattlemen whose men had had run-ins with the law, and who publicly had criticized Wyatt Earp, made practically the same statements.

Other denials followed, until within a week hardly anyone was left who could have made the offer. Without any question, it had been made, but public sentiment had forced the man who made it to retract his words.

The season rolled on. Below the Deadline in Dodge, anything went, so long as a killing wasn't involved. But north of the railroad tracks, Dodge was respectable. North of the tracks, men checked their guns at the first place they stopped, and behaved in an orderly fashion. It was either that, or a night in jail and a stiff fine in the morning.

A church was built and a school was opened. The city council discussed the development of a park. Now and then a spot of trouble would flare up, but Earp's men were quickly on the scene to handle it. Sometimes the handling of a problem involved a trip across the tracks to one of the joints below the Deadline, but even there a marshal was respected.

"Things are growing a little too quiet for me," Bat Masterson complained one night. "I feel I'm getting rusty."

"Then why not run for county sheriff?" Wyatt said. "Charlie Bassett told me the other day he wasn't going to run again."

"County sheriff?" Bat said. "I'm only twenty-two."

"But folks around here like you. I think you could be elected."

"Who would you get to take my place as one of your deputies?"

"I think Jeff Crandall will be about ready for such a job next year, after the election."

"He's younger than I am," Bat said.

"This is a young man's country. Besides, he handles himself well."

"Yep, he's steady enough," Bat agreed. "Such a thing might work out all right—if I could be elected as sheriff."

"Think it over," Wyatt said, "If you—"

They kicked open the door and went inside. There were maybe twelve or fifteen men in the barnlike room. The lanterns hanging from the ceiling didn't give much light. Wyatt's eyes passed from one man to another. He didn't see Bill Driggs anyplace, but Slinger Jack was here, scowling at them from the table where he sat. A mountain of a man, fat but powerful. Tall, red-faced, and with an ugly scar on his cheek.

Wyatt walked toward him, aware of the silence which had swept over the room. He said, "Slinger, we're looking for Bill Driggs."

"Never heard of him," Slinger said.

"He wouldn't be hiding in one of your back rooms, would he?"

Slinger came ponderously to his feet. "I told you I never heard of him, Earp. Are you calling me a liar?"

"Should I?" Wyatt asked.

"It's about what I'd expect," Slinger answered. "No one living can match your draw. When you're wearin' your guns you can say anything you want to and get away with it. Someday I'll catch you without your guns, and when I do—"

"When you do—what?"

"When I do, I'll take you apart, Earp. I'll take you apart with these two hands."

He raised them and looked at them. They were big hands, big knuckled, powerful.

There were two back rooms here in Slinger Jack's. The door to each one was closed. Wyatt thought there was a good chance that Driggs might be hiding in one of those back rooms, but he was sure that unless they could get Driggs under their guns, he would make a fight of it, and someone besides the fighters might get hurt.

Another possibility occurred to Wyatt. Slinger Jack was begging for a fist fight. If he accepted the man's challenge and took off his guns, and if Driggs was in one of the back rooms, the excitement of the fight might give the gunman a perfect opportunity for a shot at him, and at Bat Masterson as well.

"What's the matter, Earp?" Slinger Jack was asking. "Are you afraid to take off your guns?"

"Not at all," Earp said, and stepped closer to Bat.

"What's the idea?" Bat growled. "I wouldn't break a fist on him."

"Just keep an eye on the others here in the room, and see that they don't interfere," Wyatt said. And then in

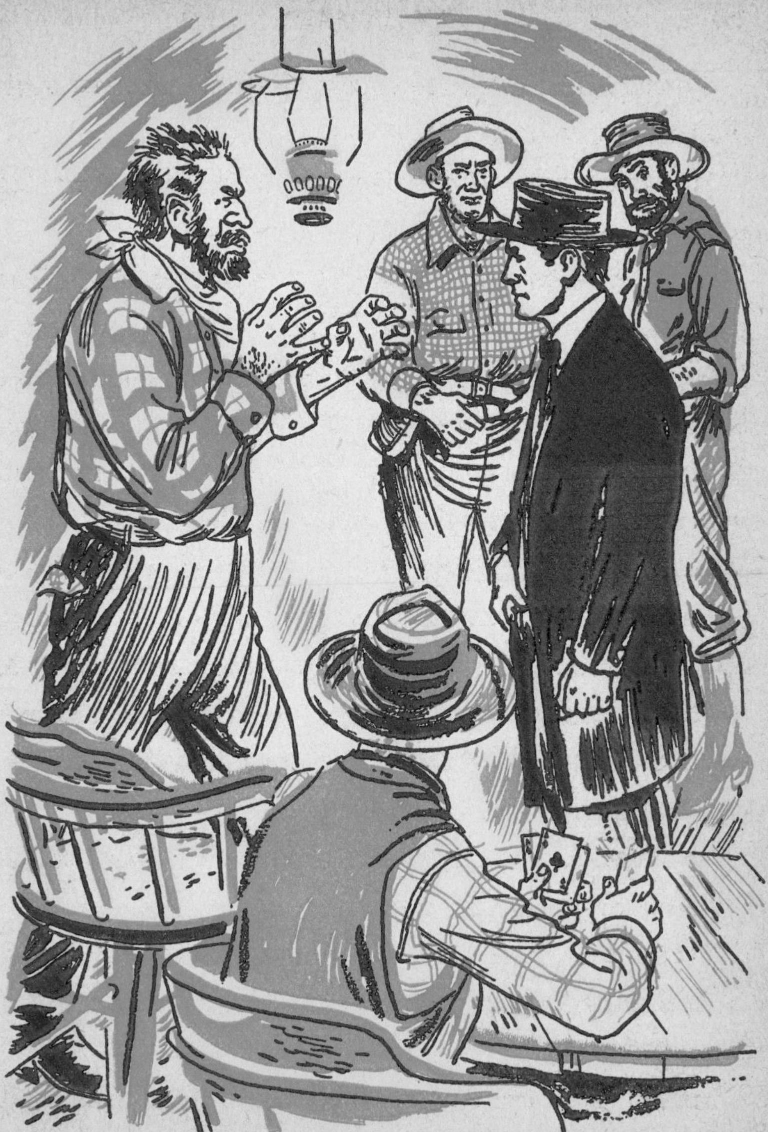

a lower voice, *"Watch the back doors!"*

Slinger Jack had given a loud whoop of delight and had peeled off his coat. He was ordering the tables pushed back out of the way.

"But this won't take long," he boasted. "It won't take long at all."

Wyatt took off his coat and laid it on a chair near where Bat was standing. He unbuckled his gun belts and folded them on top of the coat, noticed that Bat was standing where he could watch the back doors as well as the crowd in the room, then turned to face Slinger Jack.

Wyatt was thin, slender, and although over six feet tall, Slinger Jack towered above him by several inches. His opponent also had a weight advantage of much more than a hundred pounds. Wyatt knew that to some of the men watching, it didn't seem as though he had a chance. But he had been in fights such as this before. He doubted that the Slinger could match his speed or the perfect co-ordination of his muscles. At any rate he soon would find out.

Slinger Jack had removed his gun belts and knife, and now with a bullish roar, anticipating an easy victory, he rushed forward.

Wyatt sidestepped. He whipped a sharp blow into the

Slinger's face, and as the man straightened up he followed it with three more, each one landing solidly just where he aimed it.

The Slinger staggered backward. He wiped his hand across his bloody nose, then with an angry cry, plunged forward again.

This time Wyatt didn't sidestep. His fists shot out to meet the man with the full power of his body behind them. It was to Slinger Jack as though he had run headlong into a stone wall. He rocked away on his heels. He started swaying from side to side, his knees wobbling.

Wyatt stepped in and hit him again, and he went down. As he fell there was the crash of a shot from Bat's gun and Wyatt looked quickly toward the rear of the room. One of the doors, which had been pushed open a crack, opened wider. Bill Driggs staggered into the room, a gun dropping from his hand. He pitched forward on his face.

Into the silence which followed, Wyatt threw a sharp question. "Anyone else want a crack at us, either with his fists or with a gun?"

There were no takers.

Wyatt buckled on his guns, put on his coat. He walked to where Driggs had fallen, knelt at the man's side, then stood up. Driggs, who had meant to shoot him during the excitement of the fight, was beyond all human help.

But another had been involved in the plot. Slinger Jack. Wyatt returned to where the Slinger was lying. He prodded him with his boot. The Slinger groaned. His eyes blinked open. He made an effort to sit up and finally managed it.

"Slinger, you'd better pack up and head for other parts," Wyatt said bleakly. "If you don't, next time I come down here we'll do this all over."

Slinger Jack mumbled something indistinctly. He was leaning forward, holding his head in his hands.

Wyatt glanced at the others in the room. He said, "One of you fellows take care of Driggs. And pass the word along Texas Street that from now on the law's going to reach over here quite often, and if men don't want to run into trouble, they'll start checking their guns and behaving themselves."

"Even down here below the Deadline?" someone asked.

"Yep. Even below the Deadline," Wyatt said. "Dodge is growing up."

14 • A TOWN IS TAMED

In the spring, Bat Masterson was elected county sheriff. This left a vacancy on the marshal's staff which Wyatt had meant to offer to Jeff. For the first time in several years, however, Jeff wasn't with him. A few months before, Wyatt's brother, Morgan Earp, had asked Jeff to accompany him on a trip to Montana, where a new mining area was being developed.

The trip had appealed to Jeff. He was tired of work around the cattle pens. He had saved a little money which might profitably be invested. And he was sure that for another few years, anyhow, Wyatt wasn't going to be interested in going into the cattle business. For these reasons, he had gone west with Morgan Earp.

To fill the vacancy on his staff, Wyatt chose Frank McLean, and then awaited the arrival of the first herds of the year to come up the trail from Texas. The season just ahead was to be the greatest cattle-shipping season Dodge had known.

But it was an orderly season compared to the year before. There still was a Deadline, below which the cowboys were allowed certain liberties. However, Wyatt and his deputies now prowled below the Deadline, holding all celebrations in order.

There were a few who challenged the authority of the law, but not many. Wyatt Earp, marshal of Dodge, was a man who had come to be respected, and it was quickly learned that those who worked as his deputies were cut of the same cloth.

Wyatt still held his appointment as a deputy United States marshal, and had, since his days in Wichita. He hadn't expected ever to use it again, but in the fall of the year, he was asked by the government to help break up an outlaw band operating in Texas. The summer had been quiet, and with winter coming on there didn't seem to be any reason why he couldn't get away. Ed Masterson agreed to take over his duties as marshal, and after promising the mayor to return as soon as possible, Wyatt rode southward.

His mission took longer than he expected. It ran on into the following spring. It never was entirely finished, for as Wyatt was engaged in running down the last members of the outlaw band, he received a wire from the mayor of Dodge.

The wire brought him shocking news. Ed Masterson, who had taken his place as marshal, had been shot and killed. And having killed the marshal of Dodge, the lawless element among the cowboys was making the most of it. Guns again were being worn openly, north of the old Deadline. Gun fights on Front Street were a daily occurrence. Law and order had been broken down completely.

Wyatt lost no time in heading back to Dodge.

He got there early in the morning of May twelfth and reported at once to the mayor, where he again pinned on his marshal's badge.

"The boys just aren't up to the job they've got to do without someone to lead them," the mayor said. "After the other side got the upper hand, they just caved in, let things drift."

"What about Bat Masterson?" Wyatt asked.

"He's got his hands full of problems out in the county,"

He broke off, startled by the sound of shooting up the street. They looked that way. Men were boiling out of the Alhambra. Three additional shots followed in rapid succession. While the echoes of those shots were still ringing in their ears, Wyatt and Bat started running for the Alhambra.

Inside on the floor, an unarmed man lay dead. He was a cowhand wearing an empty holster. He had checked his gun.

A man who had seen what had happened gave Wyatt the story.

"It was Bill Driggs who shot him," the man said. "Driggs had checked his gun here, earlier. He came in to get it, as he was planning to leave town. Then he saw this fellow, and he shouted, 'Baker, I've been looking for you.' And he pulled his gun and shot him through the head.

"After that, he seemed to go crazy. He shouted, 'Where's Earp? I want to kill Wyatt Earp,' and fired three more shots in the ceiling. Men started leaving here fast. He rushed to the back door. He stopped when he got there and yelled, 'Tell Earp I'll be at Slinger Jack's, below the Deadline. And that I'll be waiting for him.' Then he left."

Wyatt nodded soberly. He knew Bill Driggs, had twice

arrested him for disturbing the peace. And he knew Slinger Jack's place below the Deadline. It was the headquarters for the roughest element that came up the trail. Slinger Jack, himself, fitted into the same category. He wore two guns, but it was said he preferred using the knife he wore belted in front of his fat stomach.

"Let's go," Bat said.

Wyatt nodded. He matched Bat Masterson's long strides as they headed for the lower part of the town, and he was half hoping, as they walked that way, that Slinger Jack would give them some excuse to run him in, too.

It was dark and shadowy along Texas Street. The two men passed several noisy places and came finally to Slinger Jack's, which seemed unusually quiet.

"Good spot for a trap," Bat muttered.

The same thought had occurred to Wyatt. He wished, uneasily, that they had brought more men along. Charlie Bassett would have been glad of the excuse to come with them. Bat's brother and Bill Tilghman would regret having missed a trip below the Deadline. They could go back and get them now, but that would take time.

"Suppose we take a look inside," he said, scowling.

"That's why we're here," Bat answered.

the mayor answered. "He killed the men who got his brother and he's tried to help us here in town, but there's rustling going on, and there have been a few stage holdups, and after all, he is the county sheriff."

"Find the other deputies and send them to me," Wyatt said.

"Where'll you be?"

"Patrolling the Deadline. Relieving men of their guns when they cross into Dodge. Do you think my name means anything around here?"

"It means more than you'll ever know, Wyatt."

"Then spread word around that I'm back, and that men who come to Dodge and fail to observe the law can expect to end up either in jail, or in a pine box under six feet of earth on Boot Hill."

Wyatt left the mayor's office and walked directly toward the railroad tracks. As he neared the Deadline he met two men walking into town. Both wore their guns. He angled to meet them, and when close to them called, "Hey, there, didn't you know it was against the law to wear your guns in Dodge?"

Both men laughed. It was quite evident that they didn't

recognize him, for one of them asked, "Who's going to enforce the law? You? Where did you get that tin badge? I think I'd like it as a souvenir."

He drew his gun, but before he could cover the marshal, felt it knocked aside, and in another second, keeled over from a blow on the head.

"Don't try it," Wyatt yelled at the other man, who now was grabbing at his holster.

His gun covered the second man. He disarmed him and made him carry his companion to the lockup. A few minutes later the marshal was back at the Deadline. Three deputies joined him. By noon they had arrested eighteen men who had crossed the Deadline wearing their guns.

By this time, a crowd had assembled on each side of the Deadline, those on the north side to watch the fun, those below the Deadline to plot what course of action they should follow. The cowmen didn't want to start an open war and risk the trouble that would follow. All they wanted was the right to keep on wearing their guns, but it was clear that if they tried marching into Dodge with their guns on, someone would first have to face Wyatt Earp. There were no volunteers for such a job.

That day most men who had come to Dodge, and who

did not want to surrender their guns, stayed below the Deadline.

One other thing of note happened that morning. An awfully thin man with ash blond hair stepped out of the crowd on the north side of the Deadline and walked toward Wyatt, calling out a greeting as he came forward.

"Howdy, Doc," Wyatt answered. "Didn't know you were in Dodge."

"Sent word to you I'd be here, but maybe you didn't get it," Doc Holliday answered. "Looks like what you are doing is fun."

"Want a badge?" Wyatt asked.

"Not just yet. But if you ever need help, just yell for it."

They talked for a few minutes longer, then Doc Holliday turned away. Neither he nor Wyatt knew at that time how closely they would be associated in the future.

Doc Holliday, even then, was a famous man in the West. He had been born in Virginia, had developed tuberculosis, and in reality had come West to die. He had discovered that men in the West depended a great deal on their guns and had bought a pair and started practicing with them. He had almost the same perfect muscular coordination as Wyatt, and he soon learned how to handle his guns with remarkable speed and skill.

His illness made him irritable. He got into quarrels easily, and at the time he showed up in Dodge he had been in a long number of gun fights. His list of victories was as impressive as that of any gun slinger living.

Wyatt had met him on the trip to Texas from which he just had returned. He wasn't sure this morning that he was glad to find Holliday here in Dodge, but he put the matter out of his mind. He had more important things to think about.

They had made a good start at returning law and order to the town, but after dark they wouldn't be able to hold a patrol at the Deadline. After dark they might run into trouble, for it was a cinch the Texans didn't approve of the restoration of the old order.

That night Wyatt Earp and his deputies worked in a compact group, moving along Front Street from one place to another. They more than doubled the number of men they had jailed during the day. At several points, where one man working alone might have had trouble, five deputies, working together, found it an easy matter to enforce the law.

Within a week it was clear to everyone that in Dodge the tables had been turned. Men who rode into town now checked their guns immediately upon their arrival. The rough and rowdy element stayed on the other side of the Deadline.

But again there was talk of a price on Wyatt Earp's head, and there were rumors of an organized movement against him. On three nights running, men took pot shots at him. One such man he pursued and shot down, but this only added to the undercurrent of talk and the general uneasiness in the town.

"What are you going to do about it?" Doc Holliday asked him one afternoon.

"Ride it out until the men back of it make some move themselves," Wyatt answered.

"You know them?"

"Tobe Driscoll and Ed Morrison, two cattlemen I ran out of Wichita several years ago."

"What makes you think they'll make some move on their own?"

"They're impatient men," Wyatt said, grinning. "They will wait only so long for someone to do the job for them, then they'll try themselves."

"I hope I'm around when they do," Doc Holliday said. "I like the way you work, Wyatt."

Tobe Driscoll and Ed Morrison talked it over. Each was determined to bring about the downfall of Wyatt Earp. The problem facing them was agreement on a plan. Morrison was impatient. He wanted to collect a crowd of men and ride into Dodge and take over the town. Tobe Driscoll advocated caution.

"Forty-nine out of fifty men will turn tail and run the minute Earp steps out in the street," he insisted. "Name me anyone who's got the guts to face him."

"So he's faster with his guns than anyone living," Morrison agreed. "But what could he do if fifty of us cut loose on him?"

"Bring down ten of us."

"He's not that good."

While they were haggling about what to do, a man rode up to their camp with word that Earp had left Dodge the day before, on a trip with the sheriff, which might keep him out of town most of the week.

Driscoll's eyes widened with interest. "Here's our chance, Morrison."

"What do you mean, our chance?" Morrison replied. "We've got to wait for him to come back, don't we?"

"Sure, but where will we wait? Right in Dodge."

"What do you mean?"

"I mean this. That without Earp to help them, the other deputies can be pushed over. All we've got to do is ride into Dodge with our guns and dare anyone to do anything about it. Earp's crowd won't buck us without him. And once we show people we can take over, everyone south of the Deadline will follow us. When Earp gets back he'll be walking into an inferno. He won't last long enough to get halfway down Front Street."

It was too late to ride on Dodge that day, but by the next afternoon Driscoll and Morrison were ready. They had picked twenty-five men to serve as the hard core of their army. The had lined up a plan. They would stop, first, below the Deadline, pass out word of what they intended doing, then move into Dodge and run Earp's deputies out of town. By the time they had taken charge of the place, a hundred armed men would have drifted after them.

Morrison never had felt better. "We'll give Dodge a real Texas-style hurrah," he boasted. "If there are any windows left in the town tomorrow, I'll eat 'em."

"And if there are any deputies left in town, I'll eat 'em," Driscoll said laughing.

At the head of their twenty-five men, they rode in the direction of Dodge.

When Wyatt Earp rode out on a chase with the sheriff, he wasn't sure how long they would be gone, or how wise it was that he should leave. But the emergency was a real one and he owed the sheriff too many favors to turn him down.

Luck was with them. They completed their mission in record time, and got back with their prisoners toward dusk of the third day.

As they were locking them up, Wyatt heard the sudden sound of shooting from the direction of Front Street, and he wasted no more time at the jail. Later he was to learn the details of what had happened. The crowd led by Morrison and Driscoll had reached Dodge and stopped for supper below the Deadline. They had left their horses there, and now, at the dinner hour, were crossing into the main part of the town, shooting up the street as they moved ahead. Doing it in real Texas fashion, cutting loose with their guns, and rebel yells, and smashing up some of the places as they moved along.

When Wyatt left the jail and started running toward Front Street, he had no idea he was going to be up against a crowd of bitter, determined men. He thought maybe a new trail crew, just up from Texas, had hit town. He had dealt with such outfits before, and would again. It usually wasn't too difficult to talk sense to the leader and get his help in handling his men.

The sky was still gray when Wyatt reached Front Street, and there was enough remaining light to show him the crowd of cowboys marching forward. He realized immediately that ordinary methods would not work this time. But a shotgun might, and he had one, loaded and ready, in the Long Branch on the next corner.

He hurried that way, but two men coming up the street reached the door to the Long Branch just before he did. Too late to avoid them or duck out of sight, he recognized them as Tobe Driscoll and Ed Morrison. Their guns were in their hands, and swung suddenly to cover him.

Wyatt stopped. He was only three paces from the door, and in the shadow of the building. And for an instant, neither Driscoll nor Morrison guessed who he was.

"Get your hands up," Morrison barked. "And pull away

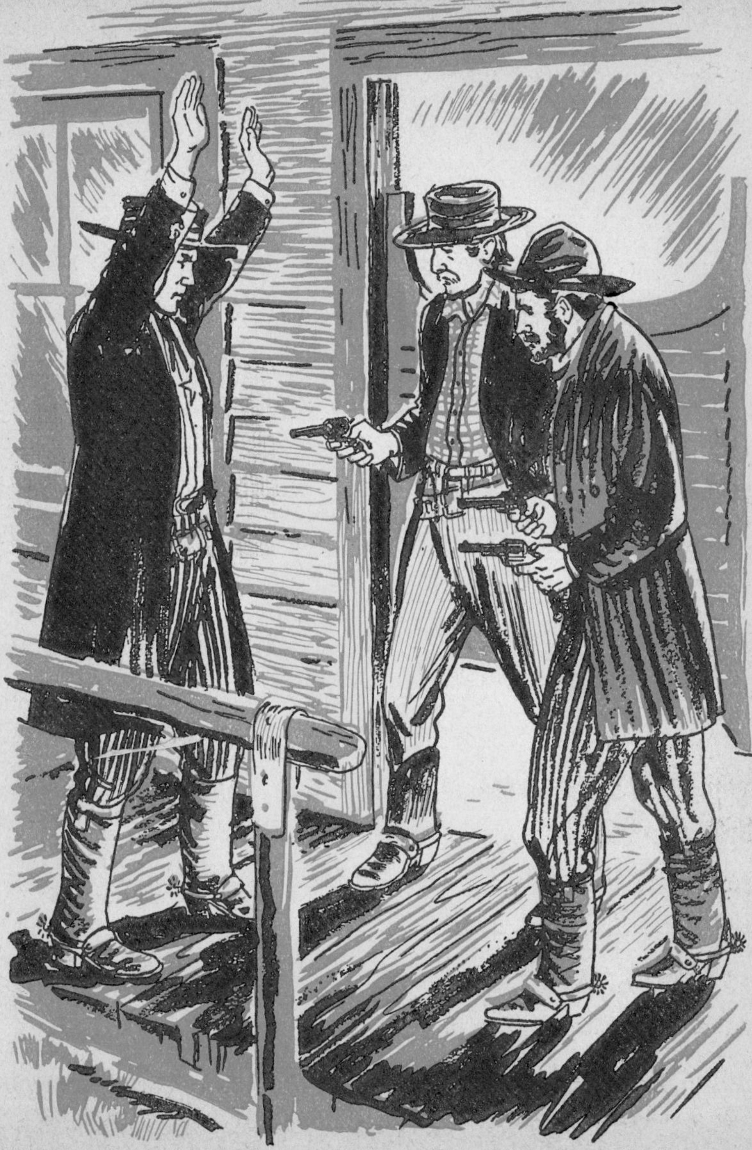

from here. We've taken over the town tonight. We've—"

His voice broke off. His guns wavered. He suddenly had recognized the man he was covering.

"It's Earp!" Driscoll shouted.

"It sure is," Morrison gasped.

His guns steadied again as he realized he had command of the situation. Earp's guns were holstered. All he had to do was fire the guns he was holding, and the man he hated, and had feared, would die. But a situation like this was one to be enjoyed.

"Earp," he shouted, "I'm going to kill you. I'm going to fill you so full of holes there won't be much of you left to be carried away. Jerk your guns, you so and so. Let's see how fast you really are."

Others had come up. Other guns now covered him. Fast as he was, Wyatt knew he couldn't draw his guns swiftly enough to stop all the shots of the men in the street. He might get Morrison, or Driscoll, but surely they, or someone else, would bring him down.

He stood motionless, waiting. He never had been in a corner quite so tight as this. He could sense the temper of the men facing him. They felt safe. They weren't going to back down. The fear of death which had paralyzed Ben

Thompson, and Mannen Clements, couldn't touch them, for they had him gun-covered and at their mercy. At any moment now, one of them would fire.

There was a movement in the doorway of the Long Branch. A slight, thin figure stepped out on the walk. It was Doc Holliday. He held a gun in each hand, one leveled at Morrison, one at Driscoll.

"Count me in on this, boys, at Wyatt Earp's side," he shouted. "Drop your guns or I'll drop you."

Doc Holliday couldn't command the others in the street any more than Earp might have done, yet he commanded the lives of Tobe Driscoll and Ed Morrison. They had made the fatal mistake of devoting all their attention to Wyatt Earp. They hadn't anticipated that anyone would be foolish enough to interfere.

Morrison and then Driscoll glanced at Doc Holliday. They were from Texas. Doc Holliday had made his reputation as a gun slinger down in Texas. They both recognized him. They knew what he could do with his guns. They knew that as things stood now, they were as dead as Earp was. If firing started, others in the street might get Earp and Doc Holliday, but the two Texan leaders wouldn't live to know about it.

"Drop your guns," Holliday ordered again. "Be quick about it."

All the stiffness went out of Morrison's body. He dropped his guns. Driscoll hesitated a moment more, then shrugged and let the guns he was holding fall to the ground.

"Now what about the rest of 'em, Wyatt?" Doc Holliday asked.

Wyatt whipped up his .45's, swinging to face the men who had come here with Driscoll and Morrison.

"Toss your guns in the street," he shouted. "Then line up, your hands above your head."

A man at the far edge of the crowd snapped a shot at Doc Holliday. He made the mistake of not shooting straight enough. Holliday's answering shot knocked him to the ground. With this example to look at, the others offered no more objections. They surrendered their guns, and Wyatt marched them to the lockup with Morrison and Driscoll.

The next day, all would be fined and ordered to leave Dodge and not return. They would do just that.

This was the last organized raid on Dodge. In the days ahead, occasionally a man would get out of line and have to be jailed, but never again would there be any serious challenge to the forces of law and order. New men coming up the trail were warned that Wyatt Earp would stand for no nonsense, and then were told that in case the marshal of Dodge needed any extra help, he could call for it in the person of Doc Holliday.

Wyatt Earp and Doc Holliday! Who could be so foolish as to buck such men! It was safer to spit at a coiled rattlesnake—or perhaps it was safer just to behave, and act civilized.

The wild and woolly boom days in Dodge were at an end.

15 • THE ROAD TO TOMBSTONE

In the summer of 1879, Jeff Crandall returned to Dodge. He was a young man now, tall, thin, sun-tanned, and much more sure of himself than when Wyatt had first met him.

"How's Montana and the mining business?" Wyatt asked him. "And how's my brother Morgan?"

"Morgan's well," Jeff said. "I brought you a letter from him."

"And the mining business?"

"They say Arizona is better. That's where I'm going. Why not go with me? You have a brother out there, and soon will have two. Morgan is going to Arizona."

Wyatt was silent for a moment, then nodded. "You know, I might go, Jeff. Dodge has calmed down again. There's no real reason I have to stay here."

Jeff looked pleased. "We could all throw in together. Some of us could prospect, some could work. You might even get a job as marshal in the new town that's grown up where they've made the latest silver strike. A place called Tombstone."

"I don't think I'd want to be marshal," Wyatt said. "But we might start a freight line. Your coming here is part of a plot, isn't it?"

"What plot?" Jeff asked.

"A plot to get me to come to Arizona. Virgil's been writing me to come. He's in a place called Prescott."

"There's money to be made in Arizona," Jeff said defensively. "This isn't a plot exactly, but we thought—"

"All right, Jeff," Wyatt said, laughing. "We'll talk it over. It's good to see you again, whatever I do."

He had been feeling for some weeks now that his work in Dodge was over, and that the deputies now serving under him could carry on without him. This would leave him free to think of his own welfare, for a change.

A town marshal didn't make enough money to get ahead. In Arizona, if they didn't make a strike in the mining fields, he at least could go into a business that might be profitable.

Jeff didn't have to wait long for his decision. Early in September Wyatt met him on the street and asked, "Ready to travel, Jeff?"

"Any day you are," Jeff answered.

"I resigned last night," Wyatt said. "Bought two wagons."

"Wagons? Why are we going by wagon?"

"Because the farther west you get, the more expensive things are. Two wagonloads of furniture and supplies will come in handy in Tombstone."

"And the wagons can serve as the start of a freight line."

"That's right, Jeff. Think you can handle one?"

"You bet I can, Wyatt," Jeff said. "When do we leave Dodge?"

"Day after tomorrow, early. We'll be heading for Tombstone. Have you any idea how the place got its name?"

Jeff shook his head. "No, I haven't."

"I heard this story from a man who had been there," Wyatt explained. "Several years ago, a prospector named Ed Schieffelin wanted to go hunting for gold or silver in a rugged part of the country which was looked on as Apache territory. The Army warned him that if he went there, all he would find would be his own tombstone.

When he found the ore he was after and had to give the place an identifying name, that's what he called it. Tombstone."

"And where he made his strike, a town grew up."

"That's right, Jeff. It's not much of a town, yet, but the man I talked to the other day said people were headed there from all over the country. That's one thing about it I don't care for."

"Why?"

"A boom town like Tombstone attracts a good many people who are willing to work for their money. It attracts others who are not. Outlaws, gun slingers, gamblers, men who rob and kill. Hope they have a good marshal in Tombstone."

"I know a good one who will be heading that way, day after tomorrow," Jeff said laughing.

"Nope. I'm through with that work," Wyatt said.

He was wrong. In Tombstone, and as a United States marshal, he was going to go up against the toughest crowd he ever had had to face.

Two weeks out of Dodge, Doc Holliday joined them, and by early November they reached Prescott. There Doc

Holliday found a job which interested him, but Wyatt's brother Virgil took his place in the little caravan with another wagon, and they drove on, Doc Holliday promising to catch up with them later.

Tucson was their last stop before Tombstone, and in Tucson they met the sheriff of Pima County, a man named Charles Shibell. He seemed delighted that Wyatt had come to Arizona.

"You're just the man I've been looking for," he said earnestly. "I need a deputy sheriff in Tombstone."

"But not me," Wyatt said. "I'm going to run a stage line."

"You're too late for that. They have two stage lines operating out of Tombstone right now. They don't need any more."

"Then I'll carry freight," Wyatt said.

He wouldn't listen to the sheriff's proposition, and that afternoon he set out to find a place where a corral could be built. He would need a corral, office, and storage sheds, both here and in Tombstone.

While he and Jeff were considering a vacant area at the head of the main street, three men approached them. One was gaunt, bearded, round-shouldered. He had the wrinkled face of an old man but his eyes still were sharp, clear, piercing. The two other men were younger. All were heavily armed.

It was the older man who spoke. "Is your name Earp?"

Wyatt nodded.

"I'm N. H. Clanton," the old man said. "Maybe you've heard of me."

"Yes, I've heard of you," Wyatt said.

Even in Dodge, men had spoken of Old Man Clanton. He was a renegade from Texas justice, had been run out of California by a vigilante committee, and finally had settled in the San Pedro Valley in Arizona with his three sons, Ike, Phin, and Billy, all three raised as outlaws.

Around them, the Clantons had drawn every bad man who had come to the territory. The old man was their chief. It was said that he could call on a force of three hundred riders, if he needed that many.

There was no type of banditry in which the Clantons were not expert. They held up and robbed stages. They jumped mining claims. They diverted freight wagons to their own use. They rustled and resold cattle, mules, and horses. They levied tribute on the honest cattlemen in the region. Any who opposed them died, and died quickly of "lead poisoning," a bullet fired in the night.

Yes, the Clantons were widely known. And equally famous were some of the outlaws who rode with them. Curly Bill, Johnny Ringo, Frank and Tom McLowery, Pony Deal, Frank Stillwell, Sam Spade, and Joe Bundy.

Old Man Clanton was leaning forward, his hands on his hips, his bearded chin poked forward aggressively.

"I've got a message for you, Earp," he said. "It's a friendly message from some friends of mine, and here it is. *Get out of Arizona. We don't need you here.*"

Wyatt pushed back his hat. He glanced from Old Man Clanton to his two companions. He was looking at Curly Bill and Johnny Ringo, but he didn't know it.

"Well?" Clanton asked sharply.

"I like it here," Wyatt said. "I'm staying."

Jeff stood quietly at Wyatt's side, his hands near his guns. He had learned to pull his Colts with an amazing speed. Now he was ready for anything that might happen.

For a minute it looked as though they were in for a gun fight, but he and Wyatt made two against three, and Old Man Clanton preferred the odds more in his favor.

"Get out of here, Earp," he said gruffly. "Or stay here an' get buried."

He turned abruptly and walked away. Curly Bill and Johnny Ringo followed him.

That night Wyatt saw the sheriff again, and again the sheriff pressed him to take a deputy's badge.

"You won't have any responsibilities in Tombstone," the sheriff said. "They're organizing the town and are going to appoint their own marshal. Your work will be in the county. Half the bullion shipped from Tombstone doesn't reach its destination. Clanton's men divert the wagons to their own camp. Hardly a stage pulls out that isn't held up. If you run a freight line, what about your own wagons?"

"My wagons will get through," Wyatt said.

"Take the badge anyhow," the sheriff insisted. "If you change your mind, pin it on."

On that basis Wyatt accepted the deputy's badge. He didn't think he ever would wear it, but as things worked out, he did.

They left the next morning for Tombstone, and at their first night camp, held a sobering conference. In view of Old Man Clanton's warning, it seemed quite likely that they would run into trouble somewhere along the road. It didn't seem wise to leave it, for this Arizona country was cut by arroyos, many of which would be hard to cross. And it was a good bet that when the Clantons hit them, they would hit in force.

"But so far as I'm concerned, I don't intend to surrender these wagons," Wyatt said. "How do you two feel?"

"Just tell us what to do," Virgil said.

Jeff nodded. "You're calling the turn, Wyatt."

"Then I should have a clever plan," Wyatt said. "But I don't. I think they'll hit us by day. Since I'm driving the lead wagon, if they hit us by day and I see them coming, I'll turn my wagon enough so you can see me. When I throw up my hands, it won't be in surrender. It will be a signal."

"A signal to do what?" Jeff asked.

"To roll back from your seat into the bed of the wagon. We each have a shotgun and two rifles. Keep them just behind you, loaded and handy. When you roll back into the wagon, grab them and start firing. I'll be doing the same. I'm banking on this. The Clantons have been having everything their own way. They won't be expecting a fight."

The Earp wagon train rolled on undisturbed, and Wyatt was beginning to feel he had been wrong in his estimate of the Clantons. Half a day out of Tombstone, however, the outlaws made their attack, sweeping down on them from the crest of a low hill.

Wyatt turned his wagon at an angle across the road, so that Virgil and Jeff could see him. He glanced at the shelter he had built behind the seat. It was lined with sacks of flour and his guns were handy. Jeff and Virgil each had such a hole to flop into when the shooting got under way.

There were twenty to twenty-five men in the crowd riding down the hill. They held their rifles aloft, and were shouting. Wyatt realized that when they reined up, those rifles would cover him and Virgil and Jeff, and that if they showed any signs of opposition, the outlaw band wouldn't be slow about firing.

But he didn't want to show his cards too soon, and so he sat waiting.

The outlaws spread out as they neared the three Earp wagons. Those in the lead reined up, and as they started to level their rifles, Wyatt's arms jerked into the air, and he threw himself backward over his seat into the shelter he had prepared. He grabbed his shotgun as he fell, and as he fired it, spraying shot at the men, he heard the boom of Jeff's shotgun and the crack of Virgil's rifle.

Wyatt fired again, emptying the other barrel of his shotgun. He reached for his rifle and brought down one of the outlaws.

The sudden defense of the three wagons, the blasting shotguns and rifles, had thrown the outlaws into a wild confusion. Their horses, many of them cut by spraying shot, were rearing, bucking, trying to wheel away. Three saddles were empty. Three men were down. Two others, badly wounded, were trying to keep from being thrown. It was impossible for the outlaws to fire accurately from the backs of their unmanageable horses. Some already were racing away.

Wyatt reloaded his rifle. He shot a gun from the hand of a man who was on the ground, aiming it his way.

Virgil and Jeff were firing as accurately as he was. This was more than the outlaws could take. Those still mounted raced away, some wounded and reeling in the saddle. They left seven men on the ground behind them. Three of the seven didn't seem to be hurt, but had had their horses shot from under them. They stood now with their hands above their heads.

Wyatt climbed out of his shelter and over the wagon wheel to the ground. Jeff and Virgil joined him. They approached the three men whose hands were in the air.

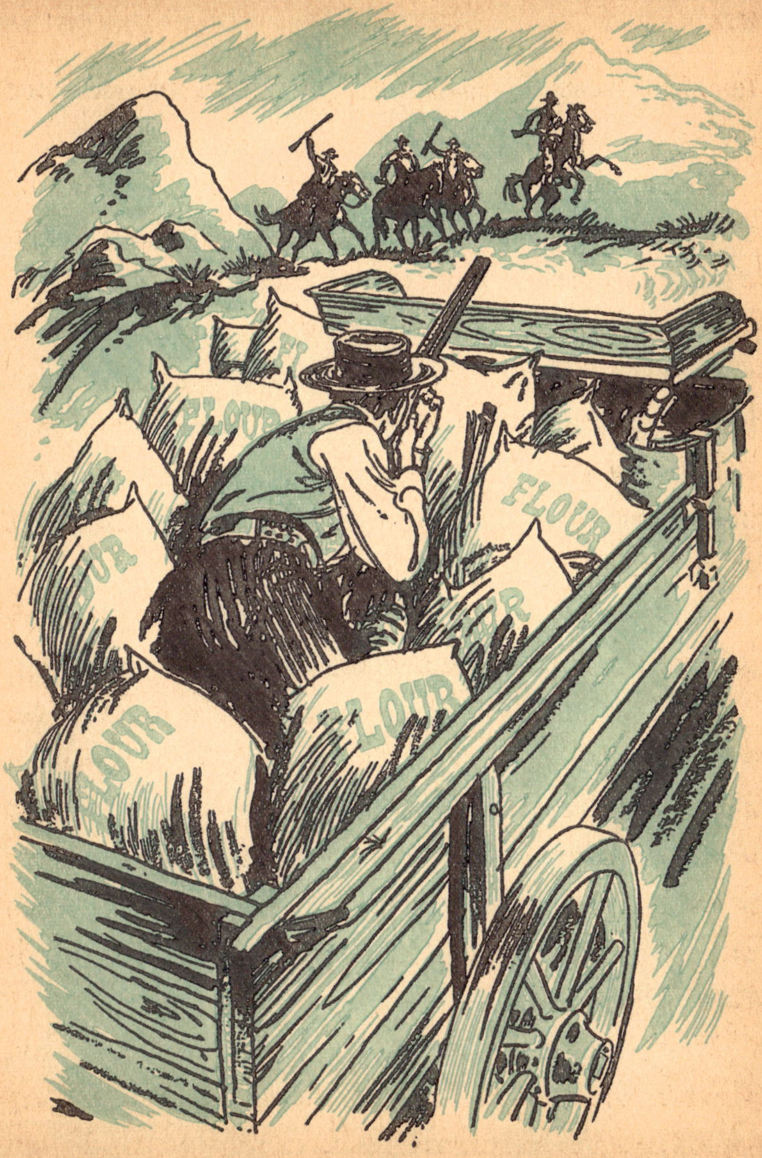
FLOUR
FLOUR
FLOUR
FLOUR

All three were bearded, middle-aged, and had a dirty, unkempt look about them. They seemed dazed at what had happened.

"Jeff, suppose you collect all the guns you can find," Wyatt ordered. "Virgil, there are a couple wounded horses you can take care of."

Jeff and Virgil turned away to do as Wyatt had asked. Wyatt stared at his three prisoners. One was slightly wounded in the arm. Nearby, another wounded man was groaning. On the crest of the hill, out of rifle shot, the outlaws who had escaped had reined up.

"What are your names?" Wyatt asked crisply.

The three men identified themselves, giving names which meant nothing to Earp, but which he would remember.

"I ought to treat you as you would have treated me," Wyatt said. "But I'm not even going to take you in. I'm not in the law business. We're driving on. Look after your dead and wounded."

He walked back to his wagon, and after Jeff had finished collecting the guns on the ground and Virgil was ready, he drove on.

The two other wagons followed.

From a distance he looked back. The outlaws had returned to the scene of the fight and were loading the dead and wounded on their horses. It occurred to him that they might try another attack, but they didn't. They rode off to the southeast, toward the San Pedro River.

The Clantons had had their first brush with Wyatt Earp. They didn't like it, but they had been the real rulers of this part of the country for so long, they weren't actually worried. "Lead poisoning" could take care of Wyatt Earp, just as it had taken care of others who got in their way.

16 • LEAD POISON

In their stronghold on the San Pedro River, the Clantons discussed what had happened. The lesson which had been arranged for Wyatt Earp had backfired. They had suffered a humiliating defeat. Men would hear of it, and all along the line the opposition would stiffen.

In the face of a situation such as this, there was only one thing to do. Wyatt Earp must be removed, and there could be no delay about it. If they struck back quickly enough, other men would realize that to defy the Clantons meant death.

"Who will handle the job?" Old Man Clanton asked. "Who wants to go after Earp?"

He had a dozen volunteers, for this wasn't a case of matching one man against another. A bullet through the back would kill as quickly as a bullet through the chest.

Two men were chosen, Sam Spade and Joe Bundy. Both were deadly with rifle or Colt. Joe Bundy was wanted by the sheriffs of a dozen different towns. Spade's record was almost as black.

A price was discussed and agreed upon, and the two headed for Tombstone.

When Wyatt, Virgil, and Jeff drove their wagons into Tombstone, its boom days were just starting. It boasted then of not more than a dozen one-story adobe cabins, but more buildings were going up, some built with lumber wagoned in from as far away as Tucson. And all around were shacks and tents or wagon homes in which close to five hundred people were living.

In another year there would be ten thousand people in Tombstone. In two years the population would be fifteen thousand.

Wyatt bought lumber and, with Jeff and Virgil to help him, and with two hired men, started building a house. His brother Morgan showed up from Montana, and a day or two later Doc Holliday rode in.

His party now seemed big enough to start freighting operations, so he contracted with a miner to deliver ore to the mills in Charleston, where he would pick up a load of lumber for the building going on here.

Morgan would drive the wagon and Wyatt would ride as the guard on the trip out. Jeff and Virgil would continue with the house they were building, then start another one. Doc Holliday would drum up more business for the freight line.

The trip to Charleston and back was uneventful, and when Wyatt returned, Doc Holliday had more trips lined up for him. But he also had important information.

"There are two men in town who have been asking about you," he mentioned. "They don't look like the kind of men who would be your friends."

"Have they got names?" Wyatt asked.

"Sam Spade and Joe Bundy."

"Never heard of them."

"Ike Clanton was in town the other day. He seemed to know them."

"Where do you reckon they are right now?"

"Somewhere along Allen Street, I suppose."

"Let's have a talk with them."

Holliday's gaunt face showed its crooked grin. "Good idea, Wyatt."

They walked down Allen Street on which a dozen new buildings had been completed and where a dozen more were going up. Before another year had passed, Allen Street would come to be known as the most violent and dangerous street in the West, but this afternoon it was a beehive of orderly activity.

They stopped at several places, and finally in the Bonanza, Doc Holliday pointed out the two men. They were seated at a table drinking. Both were big men.

Wyatt walked up behind them, touched each man on the shoulder, and as they jerked around to stare at him, he asked, "Are you the two men who are looking for Wyatt Earp?"

He didn't look like a dangerous or forceful person. He still was slender, youthful, and he had spoken in a low voice. It might have occurred to them that here was someone who could lead them to the man they were after.

"Sure, we want to see Earp," Spade nodded. "Where is he?"

"Right here," Wyatt said. "That's my name."

Both men came quickly erect. This wasn't the way they had wanted to find Wyatt Earp, or the way they had planned to handle him. He didn't look, however, as though he would be hard to handle. His hands were nowhere near his guns.

Sam Spade decided to take a chance. He clawed at his holster. At the same time Bundy made a grab for his gun.

Wyatt reached out. He smashed their heads together, then whipped up his gun and brought it down across Sam Spade's temple. It seemed to bounce from there to the side of Bundy's head. Both men sank to the floor.

A dozen paces away, a man with gray whiskers, long a friend of Old Man Clanton's, saw what was happening and recognized Wyatt Earp. He drew his Colt and aimed it, but before he could pull the trigger, Doc Holliday, whose eyes were raking the room, saw him and saw what he meant to do. A bullet from Holliday's gun ripped into his shoulder and dropped him.

"Sorry, Wyatt," Doc Holliday said. "I know you don't like shooting, but there wasn't time for anything else."

Wyatt glanced at the man Holliday had shot, then at the two lying on the floor, unconscious from the blows of his gun. He motioned to the proprietor.

"When these men wake up," he ordered, "tell them to get out of town. And tell them to tell the Clantons to leave me alone, or someone's going to get hurt."

Wyatt and Morgan Earp, with Jeff riding as an extra guard, made another wagon trip, this time to Tucson and back. They were gone ten days, but if the Clantons knew of their trip, they didn't bother them.

When they got back to Tombstone, the town seemed to have doubled in size, and looked wilder than Dodge in its wildest days. Virgil had a lot to tell them.

"Fred White, a former Army officer, has been appointed town marshal," he reported. "He's a good man but he never tried a job like this before. It's got him whipped. Men wear their guns in town. There are gun fights every day."

"Who stirs up the trouble?" Wyatt asked.

"Clanton's crowd. If a fight doesn't come easy, they force it."

Wyatt nodded. "If the Clantons can keep things stirred up here in Tombstone, the holdups and rustling in the county will be less noticed. I'm going to have a talk with Fred White."

"It isn't your job," Virgil pointed out.

"But in a way it is," Wyatt said. "I saw Crawley Dake while I was in Tucson. He's the United States marshal for the territory. And he appointed me United States marshal for the Tombstone area."

"I thought you weren't going to take another lawman's job."

"If I've got to fight the Clantons, I might as well make it a clear-cut issue between us."

He walked uptown to the marshal's office. Fred White seemed glad to see him.

"Things only got out of hand the last day or two," he reported. "Some of Clanton's toughest men are in town. I can't handle them alone and so far I haven't been able to find anyone to help me. Listen!"

From somewhere down the street there came the blasting sound of gunfire.

"There's an example of it," White said. "I don't know who fired those shots, but will you help me arrest them?"

"I'm your man," Wyatt said. "Let's go."

It was dark, but as they neared the point from which the shooting had seemed to come, a man standing in the shadows of a building started screaming a challenge to anyone to come and take him, at the same time firing his gun into the air.

"You close in from one side, I'll move in from the other," Wyatt said.

The man in the shadows saw them. He stepped away

from the building, and White, who recognized him, cried, "It's Curly Bill Brocius."

White wasn't without courage. He rushed straight in at Curly Bill and grabbed his Colt as it swung swiftly toward him. The gun went off and White dropped to the ground.

Wyatt dropped the outlaw by bouncing his gun off the man's head, then dropped to his knees as two shots laced at him from the darkness of a vacant lot.

"It's Earp!" someone shouted. "He got Curly Bill. Let's finish him."

Flat on the ground now, Wyatt returned the fire of his enemies. He heard a man scream as he was hit. He heard someone else running away. He crawled to where White was lying, discovered he was badly hurt, then stepped out to the street to get someone to care for him. The firing, at least for the moment, had stopped.

White was carried to his cabin. Wyatt lugged Curly Bill to jail, then returned to Allen Street, where he met his brother Morgan.

"They tell me White won't last very long," Morgan said gravely.

"So they've killed a town marshal," Wyatt nodded.

"When that happens, the lawless take over. But they won't take Tombstone. Get Virgil and Jeff and start working your way up Allen Street. Collar every Clanton man you see and throw him into jail. I'll pick up a few while you're getting started."

Before another hour had passed, Frank Patterson, Pony Deal, Billy Clanton, and the McLowery brothers joined Curly Bill in the lockup. A few more were added to this number. Others, known members of the Clanton band, fled the town.

The next day Virgil Earp was appointed temporary marshal. He hadn't wanted the job, but was persuaded to take it. And while he held it, Tombstone remained a more or less orderly town.

The days ran on. Wyatt, Morgan, and Jeff were away from Tombstone a good part of the time, riding as guards on the Wells Fargo stages. They had given up their plan to run a freight line.

And the Clantons seemed to have given up the robbing of stages. At least they made no attempts to hold up the stages on which one of the Earps or Jeff Crandall rode as guard. Nor did the Clantons come to Tombstone as often as in the past. The town of Charleston was nearer their San Pedro stronghold and there were no Earps in Charleston to worry about.

Doc Holliday kept busy in one enterprise or another. He talked of going on to the Pacific Coast, but for some reason or other kept putting off his departure.

Then one day at Charleston there was trouble. A man named O'Rourke shot and killed another man and was arrested by the Charleston marshal. A number of the Clanton outlaws were in Charleston at the time, and one of them suggested a lynching party. The marshal heard of this, and hitching a pair of mules to a buckboard, he set out for Tombstone with his prisoner.

Halfway up the long, sloping grade to Tombstone, the marshal looked back and saw a mob of horsemen following him. He lashed the mules to a faster run, but in spite of all he could do the pursuing horsemen gained ground behind him.

The chase continued. For a time the marshal didn't think he would make it to Tombstone before the mob caught up with him, but he did, there turning his prisoner over to Virgil Earp.

"There's a crowd on their way here to lynch him," the

marshal said. "Clanton's crowd."

Virgil sent a man for Wyatt and Morgan, who were at the Wells Fargo office.

"The Clantons don't rate very high in Tombstone," he said to the Charleston marshal. "We'll look after your prisoner for you."

Wyatt and Morgan reached his office on the run. They had heard the crowd riding into town and had guessed something unusual was happening. Virgil told them all he knew.

"We'll take the prisoner to Vogan's," Wyatt said. "It is an easy place to defend. I'll hold the front door. One of you hold the back. Morgan, you find Jeff and Doc Holliday."

They hurried with their prisoner to Vogan's, a long, narrow, adobe building, and there awaited whatever might happen.

It was late afternoon. Men were just leaving the mines. The outlaws dismounted at the edge of town, and as they started their march up the street toward the jail where they thought they would find their prisoner, it was easy to get others to join their ranks or to trail along. As they told the story, they were after a murderer, a man who needed hanging. They were close to five hundred strong when they reached the door of the jail.

There they were told the prisoner was being held at Vogan's. They turned back toward Vogan's.

In front of Vogan's, Wyatt Earp was waiting.

17 • THE FEUD

Wyatt never before had faced a mob such as this. A marching army of angry men. The rumbling of their voices as they came down the street was like a wall of sound.

Many weren't armed. And many, he knew, weren't even aware of the name of the man they had come to hang. Many in the crowd heading toward him had caught their fever of excitement from others, and later on would be ashamed of their part in what had happened.

But just as in every group, there remained a hard core of those who wouldn't easily be turned back. It was this hard core he had to deal with, and in view of the support of the others, it wasn't going to be easy.

It was a job, however, that had to be done. Give in to the mob, and law and order were dead in the town of

Tombstone, and out in the county as well.

Wyatt had taken a double-barreled shotgun from his brother's office. He held it resting over one arm. His guns were belted around his waist. Those along Allen Street below him had cleared out of sight, leaving him alone to face the mob.

He waited quietly until those in the front ranks of the mob recognized him, and started holding back. Then he raised his voice and shouted, "Stand where you are. You've come far enough."

Those in front tried to hold back, but the pressure from behind thrust them forward. The mob spread down the street, closing in below the building in which the prisoner was held, and leaving an open space circling Wyatt Earp at the door. It was the men in the rear who were the most noisy, and who kept shouting their demands that he surrender his prisoner.

"Keep back," Wyatt shouted. "There'll be no lynching today."

He didn't budge from where he stood. A sudden rush from the mob would sweep him off his feet, and he knew it, but that was a chance he had to take. Or a bullet could knock him down, but there wasn't time to worry about that. His shotgun covered the men nearest him, warning them to keep away.

A stoop-shouldered, thin, gaunt figure pushed through the edge of the crowd along the building front and moved up to join him. It was Doc Holliday. Two long-barreled Colts dangled from his hands.

"Cozy corner you're in," Holliday said. "Move over and make room for me."

Two others edged through the crowd to take their stand at his side. Morgan and Jeff. And from inside the building came Virgil. He had made the back door secure and saw no need to guard it.

Wyatt, Morgan, Virgil, Doc Holliday, and Jeff. These five faced the mob together, their guns covering the men in the front ranks. And there wasn't a man of the five who didn't guess that he might be one to go down if this went much farther.

"Break it up," Wyatt shouted. "Go on home. The man we are holding gets the same fair trial any one of you would insist on, if you were in his place."

From the back of the crowd, the Clantons started a chant. "Get the murderer! Get the murderer!" And started pushing forward.

Wyatt spotted them. "You fellows in front," he shouted. "Give way. Let them through."

There were a good many in the front ranks of the mob who weren't happy about being there, and who were glad of an excuse to push aside and let someone else face the Earps. They did so, and almost before they realized it, the Clanton crowd was face to face with the Earps.

"We want your prisoner," Ike Clanton shouted. "We're not fooling about this, Earp."

"Then come and get him," Wyatt said. "But you'll have to shoot your way past us, Ike. Do you think you will live long enough to do it?"

The five men in front of Vogan's hadn't budged, and didn't look as though they would. The Clantons knew how good Wyatt was with his gun. They knew how deadly Doc Holliday's Colts could be. They had found reason to respect the shooting ability of Virgil, Morgan, and Jeff Crandall. If they had to shoot their way inside, some of them might live long enough to hang the prisoner, but a good many of them wouldn't.

Wyatt waved his shotgun in a sweeping half circle.

"Go on home," he ordered. "If this street isn't cleared in two minutes, I'm going to start shooting."

Those near the Clantons who had joined the mob out of curiosity, or because of a temporary excitement, had had time to think. They didn't want to die in the sand of Allen Street. They started moving off. In less than two minutes, the Clantons were almost alone.

They still made up quite a crowd. Billy Clanton and the McLowery brothers were there, Curly Bill and John Ringo, Ike Clanton, and a dozen others Wyatt could have named. He leveled his shotgun at Ike.

"Time's almost up," he said clearly.

Ike Clanton had a decision to make. It wasn't easy. He didn't like backing down, but Ike never had been noted for his courage.

He shrugged, and waved his arms at his companions.

"Come on," he called. "The man we're after ain't worth it."

Then he looked at the Earps once more, and his face darkened with a futile anger. Under his breath he made a promise to return.

The prisoner the Earps had defended against the mob was moved to Tucson, and for the next few weeks, life in Tombstone continued as usual.

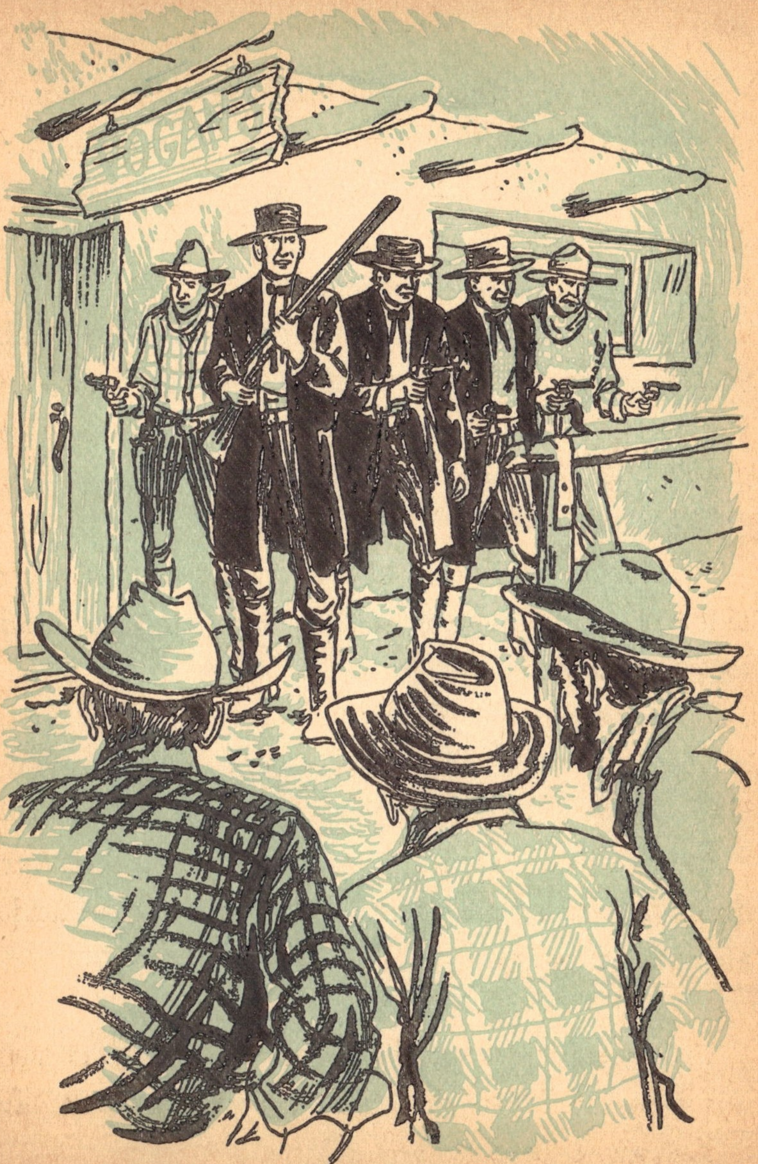

The town still was booming. Each day more people moved in, some to find rich ore and grow wealthy, some to go completely broke and end up working in another man's mine.

A town election was held and a man named Ben Sippy was elected marshal, thus relieving Virgil of a job he hadn't wanted. In the reorganization of the Arizona territory, a new county was formed, Cochise County, with Tombstone as the county seat. This made necessary the election of a new sheriff.

Wyatt was urged to run for the job, but refused. A man named Johnny Behan was elected, and Wyatt turned in his deputy's badge, but he still held his commission as United States marshal. In this connection he was often out of town on cases involving cattle rustling.

Jeff Crandall missed the close association he once had had with Wyatt, but he was busy on affairs of his own, active in building and real estate. And when Wyatt was in town, they spent as much time as they could together.

Late one evening they walked down Allen Street toward the Wells Fargo office, and as they passed the corner of the Bird Cage Theater, a man stepped out of the shadows and shoved his gun against Wyatt's side.

"Earp, I'm going to kill you," he grated. "I'm—"

Jeff had slowed down to look at the billboard in front of the theater. He was hurrying to catch up with Wyatt when the man appeared, and was only a step or two away, and on the inside. He heard what the man said, saw the gun pressed against Wyatt's side, and almost without thought, hurled himself forward.

His body struck the man waist high, and the driving force he had put into his attack carried them both to the ground. He heard the explosion of the man's gun at almost the moment he hit him, and he was sure Wyatt was dead.

The man under him was big and powerful, but Jeff gave him no time to use his greater strength. His fists, one after another, rocked against the man's head with hard, telling blows. The gunman squirmed to get free, tried to throw him off. Jeff stuck to him like a burr. He still was pounding his fists at him after the man quit his struggling, and when others in the crowd which had gathered tried to pull him off, he started fighting with them.

"Hey, take it easy, Jeff," a familiar voice was saying. "If you kill the man, how can I ask him who sent him?"

It was Wyatt who was asking the question. The man's bullet had missed him by inches. He hadn't been harmed.

Jeff looked again at the man on the ground.

"You're not going to have to ask who sent him," he muttered.

"You may be right, at that," Wyatt admitted.

The man was Charlie Knobbs, one of the Clanton crowd. Jeff had seen him in town in the company of Ike Clanton and the McLowery brothers. He once had seen him half kill a man with his fists in a fight back of the Silver Grill restaurant. He was a little amazed at what he had done.

Knobbs sat up, groaning. He fingered his puffed and swollen face, mumbling, "What happened? Who hit me?"

"A friend of mine, Charlie," Wyatt answered. "And if I hadn't pulled him off, they'd be planting you in Boot Hill tomorrow. Come on. Ben Sippy has a room at the jail for you."

He leaned over, pulled the gunman to his feet, and steered him to the jail, where Ben Sippy locked him up.

A little while later, on down the street, Wyatt and Jeff had coffee at the Oriental.

"The Clantons still are after you, aren't they?" Jeff said soberly.

"It's not me so much as what I stand for," Wyatt said. "And if it wasn't me, it would be some other man wearing a badge whom they'd be after."

"Some men with badges they've bought," Jeff said.

"Yes, that's true. There always will be dishonest policemen, but usually the men who wear a badge wear it with pride and honor."

Jeff had been thinking of the local sheriff, who had been friendly with the Clantons, and of the marshal of Tombstone, who usually managed to be somewhere else at the time of trouble. But he put that problem out of his mind. In reality, it was Wyatt Earp he was worried about.

He had hoped the Clantons had given up their plan of getting rid of Wyatt. From what had happened tonight, it was clear that they hadn't.

Wyatt reached out and squeezed his arm, smiling. He said, "Thanks, Jeff, for thinking and acting so quickly. For a moment there on the street, I thought I was a dead man. If you hadn't been with me—"

"I still owe you more than I ever can repay," Jeff said.

They were joined by Doc Holliday and Virgil, who had heard of the fight on the street. Doc Holliday was in favor of a direct attack on the Clantons.

"We ought to raise a crowd of men, head for their place on the San Pedro, and wipe them out," he said. "It'll come to that, sometime. I'm sure of it."

"It may," Wyatt agreed. "Or we may be able to pull their teeth through eliminating their leaders. Without the Old Man, Ike and Billy, and the McLowery brothers, there would be no one to hold the outlaws together."

"What about John Ringo and Curly Bill?" Virgil asked.

"They're tough enough, themselves, but they're not leaders."

"Do we ride on the Clantons one of these days?" Doc Holliday wanted to know.

"If it works out like that," Wyatt answered. "We don't take the law in our own hands, Doc. This isn't a private feud."

"It is with the Clantons."

"Then we won't have long to wait."

It seemed, a week later, as though the time Holliday had been waiting for had come. A stage to Tucson, carrying an estimated ten thousand dollars' worth of bullion, didn't reach its destination. A Wells Fargo stage, on which Jeff was riding as guard and which was headed for Tombstone, reached the scene of the holdup within an hour of the time of the trouble.

The body of the man who had been riding as guard was lying at the side of the road. He had been shot three times through the chest. The wagon tracks of the stage led off to the southeast, toward the San Pedro Valley. There was no sign of what had happened to the driver.

The minute they reached Tombstone, Jeff looked for Wyatt Earp to tell him what had happened. Fortunately, Wyatt was in town. He listened soberly to what Jeff had to say, then started asking questions.

"How far from here was the holdup?"

"An easy day's ride."

"How many men were involved?"

"I saw the tracks of four horses."

"And the wagon tracks led which way?"

"Southeast."

Wyatt nodded. He said, "Find Doc, Virgil, and Morg. Tell them to bring four days' grub and whatever guns and ammunition they think they'll need if we run into a fight. We'll leave from my cabin in twenty minutes."

In twenty minutes, Jeff, Virgil, Morgan, and Holliday were waiting at Wyatt's cabin. Wyatt joined them a few minutes later. He was scowling.

"We going after the Clantons?" Doc Holliday asked.

"We're heading for the San Pedro Valley," Wyatt said. "Where we'll end up, I don't know exactly. I gave the sheriff and the marshal a chance to ride with us. They turned me down."

"We wouldn't have had much help from them, anyhow," Virgil said.

"That isn't what bothers me," Wyatt said. "The sheriff asked me how I could be sure it was the Clantons who made off with the stage. When I told him it was a favorite trick of theirs, he still seemed doubtful. By this time tomorrow, he'll be questioning whether or not the stage really left here."

"Forget it," Morgan said. "Five of us make as big a crowd as the Clantons."

Wyatt swore them in as deputies and they rode for the San Pedro Valley. It was Wyatt's theory that to follow the Tucson road to the scene of the holdup and pick up the trail there would be a waste of time. Since the stage itself had been stolen they could be almost sure the Clantons were guilty.

Bullion shipments were in bar form, each bar weighing close to three hundred pounds. Mine owners did this to discourage holdups, for a three-hundred-pound bar was hard to handle. Individual holdup men and independent holdup bands didn't trouble themselves with bullion. Instead, they picked on passenger stages, where the passengers might have money, or they chose a stage which might be carrying a payroll sack.

The Clantons were the only crowd which specialized in the theft of bullion. They did it through the simple process of driving off the stage or the wagon in which it was being carried. They marketed it as ore from a dummy mine they said they operated.

The outlaws who rode for the Clantons posed as ranchers. Actually, they had taken over the established ranches along the San Pedro, and they did run cattle. Stolen cattle. Their main stronghold was the ranch house where the Clantons lived.

Wyatt hoped that when they picked up the tracks of the missing stage, the trail would lead to the Clanton ranch, but it didn't. Instead, it took them to the Brophy ranch.

The Brophy ranch was run by Reb Brophy and his two sons, Ollie and Pete. There was a bunkhouse at the ranch, where from two to a dozen men were quartered, the number depending on the number who needed a place to stay. How many would be there today, Wyatt didn't know.

He eyed the ranch house from a distance. He knew that by this time, the stage which had been driven here might have been burned, and the bullion hidden or transferred somewhere else. He knew that the trail itself didn't prove a thing that would stand up in court.

"Well, what do we do?" Doc Holliday asked.

"I guess we have a talk with the Brophys, if they're home," Wyatt answered.

"They're home," Jeff said. "Or at least, someone's there. I can count six saddled horses tied to the corral fence."

"Team and wagon in the yard, too," Virgil said. "It may be we got here at just the right time."

They rode on toward the ranch house which was built close to the shelter of the trees growing along the river. And those in the house saw them coming. A man stepped out on the porch, then turned quickly inside.

Wyatt drew his rifle from its boot, as did Jeff and Morgan, but Virgil and Doc Holliday didn't go to that trouble. Doc Holliday, as usual, would depend on his Colts if trouble started, and this time Virgil seemed of the same mind.

They rode into the yard and reined up. Wyatt glanced at the team and wagon. The wagon seemed half loaded with hay, but under the hay the missing bars of bullion could be hidden.

He looked at the house and called, "Brophy, come out here."

The door opened. Reb Brophy stepped out on the porch. He was a short, stocky, dirty-looking man with a ragged gray beard and watery eyes set in deep wells in his head. He wasn't wearing his guns.

"What do you want, Earp?" he asked irritably.

"We're missing a stage," Wyatt answered.

"I don't know anything about your missing stage," Brophy said.

"It was driven here."

"That's a lie."

"No, Brophy. We followed the tracks it left."

"You followed my wagon tracks."

"No, your wagon tracks are broad, the stage tracks narrow. What would be under the hay in that wagon? Bullion?"

"No."

"Mind if I take a look?"

Brophy stiffened. "You bet your life I do. I'll take no nonsense from you, Earp. Ride away while you can. You and your men are covered from both windows of my house. If I say the word, you die."

"Say it then, Brophy," Wyatt answered, "and we'll both die."

He swung his rifle to cover the man on the porch, and sat waiting. His muscles were tense. This was an old game he was playing. He had played it before and never had lost, but someday he might. If he lost today, four others would lose with him, Jeff, Morgan, Virgil, and Doc Holliday. They might get a few of Brophy's men through the windows of the ranch house, but the odds were all on the other side.

Did Brophy prize his life? That was what it hinged on and it was a trick that never had failed him.

He watched the man quite closely. He could sense the struggle Brophy was having. Brophy had stepped out here unarmed, sure of the protection his men would give him. He still could count on them, but if Wyatt Earp squeezed the trigger of the rifle he was holding, Brophy was a dead man.

"Throw down your gun, Earp," he cried hoarsely.

Wyatt shook his head. "Tell your men to fire. They may get me, but I'll get you, too. Want to bet on it?"

"I'm—I'm not armed," Brophy gasped.

"Too bad," Wyatt said.

The man on the porch took a deep breath—and made his decision. His shoulders slumped. A whipped look came into his face.

"What do you want me to do?"

"Order your men to come out here, unarmed, and with their hands raised," Wyatt said. *"And do it now."*

He whipped out the last four words in a sharp order.

Brophy did as he asked.

The bullion was in the wagon under the hay, ready for transportation to some place of storage. The stage had been driven into the barn. Wyatt had it brought out, and had it reloaded with the bullion. He asked Jeff to drive it to Tucson, with Brophy and his two sons, now under arrest, as passengers. He, Virgil, Morgan, and Doc Holliday would go along as guards.

He didn't place the other outlaws under arrest. All couldn't have been charged with the holdup, and they wouldn't have been held in jail very long. It wasn't worth the trouble of taking them in.

He asked Brophy what had happened to the driver of

the stage, but Brophy wouldn't answer him. Later, the body of the driver would be found, not far from the Tucson road.

"Wish it could have happened today," Doc Holliday said as they rode toward Tucson. "But this will do it."

"It will do what?" Wyatt asked.

"Bring on a showdown. The Clantons will have to hit back now, and they'll hit back directly at you."

Wyatt shrugged. "Maybe they will."

He thought it over and decided Doc Holliday probably was right. Men would make quite a story of the way he had invaded the outlaws' territory and recovered a wagonload of bullion. The outlaws would feel it necessary to get even, and they wouldn't waste much time about it.

The next few days would see a showdown.

18 • THE FINAL DECISION

Old Man Clanton was dead. He and a number of his men had been ambushed and shot down by a band of Mexicans, whose cattle he had stolen.

This left the control of his outlaw empire to his sons, Ike, Billy, and Phin; and since Phin was crippled and in bed from a bullet wound, Ike and Billy took active charge.

The first problem they had to face was what to do about Wyatt Earp. This was no new problem. It had been with them for some time. Various efforts had been made to get rid of Earp, but each one had failed, and after each failure they had let things ride until the next time. They were convinced, now, that this had been a mistake.

"We've got to run him out of the territory," Ike declared. "His brothers, too. And Holliday and Jeff Crandall."

"I'd rather see the whole bunch of them buried out in

Boot Hill," Billy Clanton said.

The McLowerys, who had been called in to discuss this matter, agreed with Billy. Frank and Tom McLowery hated the Earps as they never had hated anyone.

"When five men can ride into your own camp, make an arrest, and get away with the loot you've taken, it's time to do something about it," Frank McLowery said. "The Brophys must have been asleep."

"They weren't asleep," Ike said. "They were afraid of dying."

"I'm not," Frank said. "I'll take my chances with the Earps any day."

"Me, too," his brother nodded. "There's only one way to handle this. A crowd of us have got to ride into Tombstone and gun them down."

"How big a crowd?" Ike asked.

"The four of us could do it," Frank McLowery boasted.

"There are five of them, counting Holliday and Jeff Crandall."

"Then let's get Billy Claiborne. He hates the Earps as much as we do, and he's mighty fast with his guns."

"Get him," Ike said. "Tell him we're riding for Tombstone tomorrow night."

"Do you reckon they'll fight?" Tom McLowery asked. "As I figure it, the Earps are overrated."

"They'll fight or run," Ike said grimly. "This time we're going to settle things, once and for all."

Early the next evening, Virgil told Wyatt that some of the Clantons were in town, and that Ike, in particular, was boasting that he didn't intend to leave Tombstone until he had settled his score with the Earps.

"Where is he?" Wyatt asked.

"At the Oriental."

"Then let's give him his chance."

They walked to the Oriental and went inside. In the card room, Ike Clanton was complaining in a loud voice of the way he, an honest cattleman, had been mistreated by the United States marshal for the district, Wyatt Earp.

Wyatt pushed forward. He said, "Hello, Ike. I understand you want to see me."

Ike Clanton caught his breath. A sharp silence fell over the room.

"What do you want, Ike?" Wyatt insisted.

"If I had my gun—"

"Then borrow one and come outside. I'll take it away from you."

Blood rushed to Ike Clanton's face. His eyes widened in anger.

"You Earps think you run this town," he shouted. "Tomorrow you'll find out differently."

Wyatt shrugged. "All right, I'll wait until tomorrow. But if you're wise, Ike, you'll get out of town before tomorrow comes."

He turned away, realizing that Ike Clanton wasn't yet ready to make his play, but that something definitely was planned for the next morning.

"We could throw him in jail for the night," Virgil suggested.

But Wyatt shook his head. "We'll give them all the rope they ask for. Maybe when we bag Ike Clanton we can bag a few others, and end, forever, the grip the Clantons have had on this part of the country."

The next day was October 26, 1881. It was a day long to be remembered in the history of the West. It was a day of decision.

Wyatt was awakened that morning by his brother Virgil.

"They're still in town," Virgil said.

"Who's still in town?" Wyatt asked. "The Clantons?"

Virgil nodded. "And not only Ike and Billy. The two McLowerys are with them. I heard Billy Claiborne was here, too."

"That makes five."

"And there could be a few more. I haven't been downtown, but a friend came by to tell me they're boasting about what they're going to do to us."

Wyatt dressed and shaved, and then started preparing his breakfast. He remembered another time when he had been awakened this way. On that occasion it was Jeff who had come to him to tell him that Clay Allison was in town, waiting to face him. He hadn't had to shoot it out with Allison. He had buffaloed him and run him out of town, but he was afraid the Clantons couldn't be handled so easily.

Morgan joined them. He had had the same word as Virgil, but he also had a message for Wyatt from two former Army officers who now were living in Tombstone.

"They've set up a vigilante committee," Morgan said. "They want us to stay right here while they handle the Clantons. Both Captain Fronck and Captain Murray think it's time that the citizens of Tombstone took a hand in dealing with the Clanton crowd."

"And what will happen if they try it?" Wyatt asked.

"Some of them will get hurt," Virgil said.

"Anyhow, this is our fight," Wyatt said. "We are the ones who have stood in the way of the Clantons. Where is Jeff?"

"Out on a Wells Fargo run. He won't get in until tonight," Morgan said.

"And Doc Holliday?"

"Still sleeping, I imagine."

Wyatt shrugged. "We three can handle them. Where are they?"

"At the Alhambra, the last I heard," Morgan said.

"Then we'll start looking for them at the Alhambra."

Wyatt buckled on his guns, checked them, and after that stepped outside, followed by Morgan and Virgil.

All three were six feet tall and slender. They were dressed much alike, in boots, dark trousers, white shirts, black frock coats, and wide-brimmed hats. Each one wore a brace of guns.

They walked to Allen Street and turned down it toward the Alhambra.

"Not many horses tied at the hitching rails," Morgan commented.

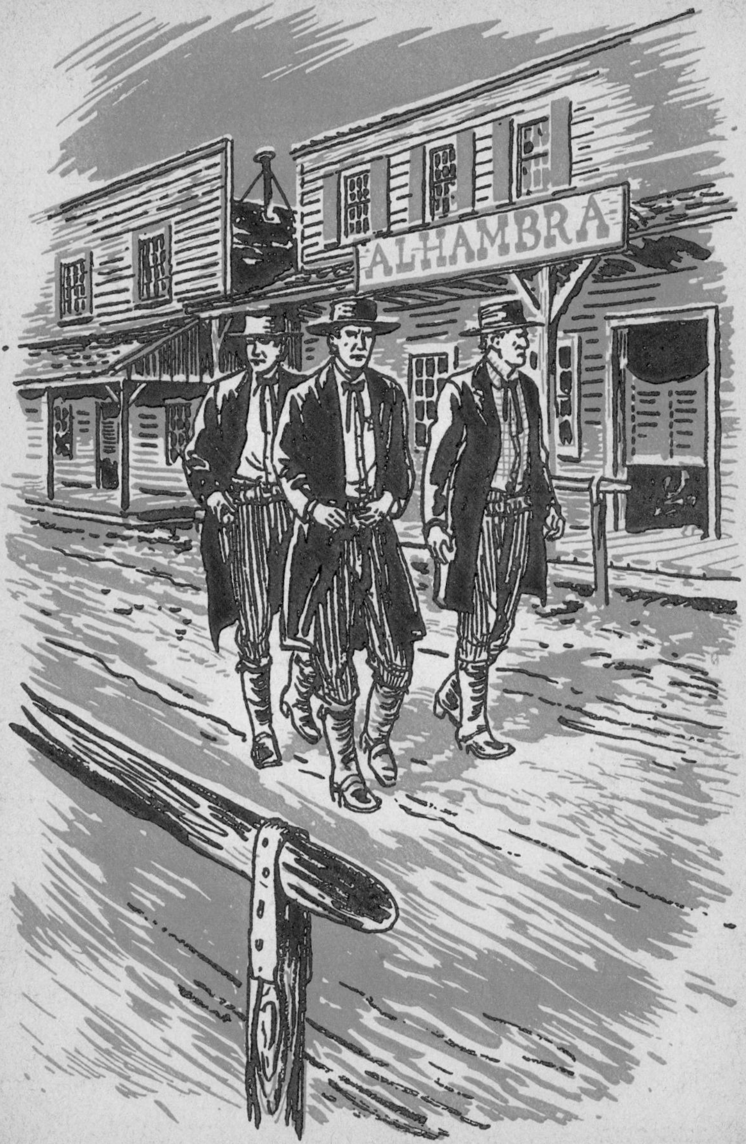
ALHAMBRA

"Not many people on the street, either," Virgil said. "Folks must have heard what's in the wind."

Wyatt nodded. His eyes raked along the street. He was wondering if the Clantons would be waiting in the Alhambra, or if they might step into sight from some other store or from a passageway.

A man standing in a doorway hailed him.

"They headed up to the O. K. Corral just a few minutes ago," he called.

"How many of them?" Wyatt asked.

"Five. Ike and Billy Clanton, the two McLowerys, and Claiborne. They said they'd be waiting for you there."

Wyatt's eyes narrowed. He wondered if that meant that the Clantons would be outside in the saddling area, or inside in the sheds. Or if this message was a trick to get them there.

Farther down the street, Captain Fronck stopped them.

"They mean business this time, Wyatt," Fronck warned. "They've been howling all night that they'd kill you this morning. They swaggered through the town as though they owned it. We can't take this kind of thing in Tombstone any longer. In half an hour I'll have fifty men ready to close in on them."

"Mob rule isn't good for a town, even if you call it vigilante rule," Wyatt said. "In half an hour, your men won't have anything to do."

"There are five of them up there at the O. K. Corral," Fronck said. "There are only three of you."

"Four," corrected Doc Holliday.

He was breathless from hurrying down the street. He scowled as he looked at Wyatt. And he asked, "Why didn't you let me know what was going on?"

"We might not walk back from this fight," Wyatt said.

"Who cares?" Doc asked, shrugging. "Count me in."

A twinkle had come into his eyes, and staring at him Wyatt realized that what he often had suspected was true. Doc Holliday loved a gun fight. He lived only for the excitement it gave him.

"I'll have my men ready in case they're needed," Fronck said.

"Do that," Wyatt said.

They moved on down the street, four in their party now, since Doc Holliday had joined them. From every door and window they passed, people were watching. Without much question, everyone knew what lay ahead. The Clantons had made threats before, but this time they seemed to have convinced everyone that they meant what they said.

A hostler from the O. K. Corral hurried to meet them. He was breathless, pale.

"Mr. Earp," he stammered, "they told me to tell you if you got out of town they wouldn't bother you."

"Thanks, Eddie," Wyatt nodded. "But we like it here in Tombstone."

They were stopped again, this time by the sheriff who had been so friendly to the Clantons.

"There's no use going ahead with this, Earp," the sheriff said. "The Clantons are a little riled up, but I had a talk with them and—"

"Did you arrest them?"

The sheriff shook his head. "They haven't broken any laws. Why would I arrest them?"

"Then I'll arrest them," Wyatt said.

"You haven't the right to."

"I still wear my badge as United States marshal."

"But the Clantons haven't broken any laws. They—"

Wyatt brushed on past the sheriff, Virgil beside him, Morgan and Doc Holliday following them. After a few more steps they moved into the street and Morgan and

Doc Holliday moved up so that they walked four abreast.

In that way they headed on toward the O. K. Corral, four tall men scuffing up the dust of the street as they moved forward.

The saddling area of the O. K. Corral was a wide open space flanked by the walls of the corral shed, an assay office, and Fly's Photograph Gallery. There was a back door into the shed, and an open alley in the rear.

Wyatt pictured this in his mind as they drew closer. He didn't know where the Clantons would be waiting. He hoped there would be a chance to talk to them, and that a fight could be avoided, but he was afraid there was going to be little time to talk.

He glanced at those with him and felt a sudden flush of pride. Morgan and Virgil both looked sober, but neither had the tight, strained lines that fear puts in a man's face. And Doc Holliday, who never seemed to have known what fear was like, was whistling under his breath. If a man had to die, he couldn't die in better company.

Step by step they moved ahead. They came even with the photograph gallery, passed it, and swung in toward the open, saddling area of the O. K. Corral.

And suddenly they could see the Clantons, each one

standing apart from the others, their back to the adobe walls of the assay office. Five men. Ike and Billy Clanton, Tom McLowery, Frank McLowery, and Billy Claiborne.

Wyatt moved steadily toward them, flanked by his brothers and Doc Holliday. The outlaws hadn't drawn their guns, but suddenly Frank McLowrey straightened up, his hands dropping swiftly to hover just above his Colts.

"You've come close enough, Earp," he shouted. "Close enough to get killed."

"Don't be a fool, Frank," Wyatt answered. "Get your hands up. We're placing you under arrest."

"I'll get my hands up like this," McLowery screamed.

He fancied himself fast on the draw. He made a grab for his guns, but as he jerked them from their holsters he saw the Colts which had appeared as if by magic in Wyatt's hands. This startled him so much that he fired hurriedly and missed. He leveled his guns to fire again, but before he could, a bullet from Wyatt's gun tore into his stomach, and he pitched forward on his face.

Other guns were roaring now. Billy Clanton was firing at them, and so were Tom McLowery and Billy Claiborne. But one of the outlaws had obeyed Wyatt's command and had shoved his hands into the air. Ike Clanton, at the last moment, had felt the breath of death on his face. He didn't want to die. This way, he might not.

To the right and to the left of Wyatt, his brothers and Doc Holliday were returning the outlaws' fire. Tom McLowery sagged to the ground, but raised himself to fire another shot. Billy Clanton was down, but was firing at them from where he had fallen.

Ike Clanton, terrified at all the shooting, was racing for the back door to the photograph gallery. Claiborne scrambled there ahead of him. Wyatt's gun swung on the two men, but he lowered it without firing another shot. He never had shot a man in the back. He never would.

As quickly as it had started, the battle was over. Wyatt looked around at his companions. Morgan had a wound in the shoulder, Virgil had been hit in the leg. Doc Holliday had a scratch across the back.

But the outlaws hadn't fared so well. Frank and Tom McLowery and Billy Clanton were dead. Ike Clanton and Billy Claiborne had escaped. Later, they would be cornered and arrested.

Wyatt put his gun away. He felt a deep relief that the fight was over. He could see that Morgan and Virgil weren't badly hurt, and he was thankful for that.

"We shouldn't have let Ike Clanton and Billy Claiborne get away," Doc Holliday grumbled.

"What of it?" Wyatt asked. "People everywhere will hear that they ran, and a coward doesn't make a leader of men. We've broken the back of the Clantons, Doc. With no one to lead them, their crowd will fall to pieces."

"There's still Curly Bill and John Ringo, and a few more."

"But there's no organized band, any longer. That's the thing to keep in mind. Individual outlaws can be handled, one at a time. It's the organized band that we have trouble with."

Wyatt Earp's analysis of the situation was true. The fight in the O. K. Corral marked the end of the Clanton band of outlaws. In the days ahead, those remaining would be accounted for, one by one. The county would elect a new and honest sheriff, and Tombstone would find a marshal who would enforce the law.

The wild days of the past were at an end.

Jeff Crandall heard about the fight at the O. K. Corral when he reached the outskirts of the town. He lost no time in going to see Virgil, then Morgan. Reassured that their wounds weren't very serious, he hunted up Wyatt Earp.

"Why couldn't you have waited until I got here?" he grumbled. "I belonged with you in that fight."

"You've grown up considerably since we met, haven't you?" Wyatt said, laughing. "Do you remember that day on the road between Abilene and Ellsworth?"

Jeff smiled. "We've a lot to remember, Wyatt."

"Yes, we have at that."

"What will be next for us?"

"Who knows, Jeff?"

"Your work here is finished."

"What do you mean by that?"

"I mean that you've shown Tombstone that law can be brought to a boom town, and that honest men don't have to live in fear of those outside the law. That's been your work, Wyatt. I think it's why you were born."

Wyatt shook his head. "I never looked on it that way. Here, and in Dodge and in Wichita, I did what I had to. That's all. I don't feel as though it was a mission."

"I do," Jeff said.

Wyatt laughed again. He put his arm around Jeff's shoulders.

"Let's go get some coffee and talk about tomorrow, or

about what we might do in the days ahead. You want to stick with me, Jeff?"

"You bet I do."

"Then maybe we'll get that cattle ranch we used to talk about, or start a freight line somewhere."

"That's what I'd like," Jeff said. "A business of our own."

They walked down the street together, two firm, longtime friends, who someday would have their business ventures together.

For Jeff had been right. The work for which Wyatt Earp was so particularly qualified was over. Tombstone was the last of the lawless towns of the old West, and with the breakup of the Clantons, Wyatt's work was done.

He didn't realize the place he had carved for himself in history, or know of the legends which would grow up around his name. If he had guessed it that night, he would have thought it foolish, and might have said, as he once said to Jeff, "A man does what he has to do. And whether it's hard or easy, he lives by the things he believes in."

Whitman
Famous Classics

- Bible Stories
- Alice in Wonderland
- Adventures of Sherlock Holmes
- Beautiful Joe
- Fifty Famous Fairy Stories
- Little Men
- Robinson Crusoe
- Five Little Peppers and How They Grew
- Treasure Island
- The Wonderful Wizard of Oz
- The Three Musketeers
- Robin Hood
- Heidi
- Little Women
- Black Beauty
- Huckleberry Finn
- Tom Sawyer

Meet wonderful friends — in the books that are favorites — year after year

Fiction for Young People

ROY ROGERS
The Enchanted Canyon
King of the Cowboys

ROY ROGERS AND DALE EVANS
River of Peril

GENE AUTRY
The Ghost Riders
Arapaho War Drums

DRAGNET

TARZAN
The City of Gold
The Lost Safari

TROY NESBIT'S MYSTERY ADVENTURES
The Diamond Cave Mystery
Mystery at Rustlers' Fort

GINNY GORDON
The Lending Library
The Broadcast Mystery

ZANE GREY
The Spirit of the Border
The Last Trail

WYATT EARP

RIN TIN TIN
Rinty
Call to Danger

WALT DISNEY
Spin and Marty

RED RYDER
The Thunder Trail
Adventure at Chimney Rock

ANNIE OAKLEY
Danger at Diablo
Ghost Town Secret

POLLY FRENCH
Of Whitford High
The Surprising Stranger

TRIXIE BELDEN
The Mysterious Visitor
The Mystery Off Glen Road

NOAH CARR, YANKEE FIREBRAND

DONNA PARKER
At Cherrydale
Special Agent
On Her Own

FURY
The Lone Pine Mystery

LASSIE
Mystery at Blackberry Bog

CIRCUS BOY
Under the Big Top

BOBBSEY TWINS
Merry Days Indoors and Out
In the Country
At the Seashore

(Whitman)

Adventure! Mystery! Read these exciting stories written especially for young readers